Almost Painless Biology

by John Abdirkin

Almost Painless Biology

COPYRIGHT 2014 by John Abdirkin and Hewell Publishing
ISBN 978-156870456-2

Sixth Edition, 2014
Printed in the United States of America

For information, contact
Hewell Publishing
2722 N. Josey Lane, Suite 100
Carrollton, Texas 75007
(972) 466-2442
(972) 466-2443 fax

Disclaimer and Limits of Liability

Table of Contents

Preface i

Course Introduction. v

Chapter 1. Organization of Nature: Chemical, Biological, and Ecological 1

Chapter 2. Photosynthesis: Producers and Consumers 13

Chapter 3. Scientific Method 19

Chapter 4. Features of Living Organisms 25

Chapter 5. Cell Players 27

Chapter 6. Evolution and Geological Time Scale 29

Chapter 7. Cell Membrane, Cell Transport and Membrane Attachments 37

Chapter 8. Cell Structures and their Functions 51

Chapter 9. Histology: The Tissues 61

Chapter 10. Entomology: Arthropods 69

Chapter 11. Plant Diversity 75

Chapter 12. Plant Anatomy. 79

Chapter 13. Seed Dispersal and Classification of Fruit 85

Chapter 14. Skeletal System: Axial Skeleton 93

Chapter 15. Skeletal System: Appendicular Skeleton 107

Chapter 16. Reproduction: Male and Female. 115

Chapter 17. Feline Dissection. 125

Chapter 18. Muscles of the Human Body and Anabolic Steroids 131

Chapter 19. Digestive System. 143

Chapter 20. Respiratory System. 153

Preface

General Biology is an introduction to the fundamental principles of life from the molecular level to the ecological community. This study guide is designed to provide the student with a better understanding of the common doctrines which control all aspects of living organisms. It has been developed to present the information clearly and concisely with a goal of meeting students' educational needs in the new millennium.

New 6th Edition

This is the sixth edition of **Almost Painless Biology**, which includes additional material to facilitate the learner in understanding the more difficult concepts. The improvements incorporated here within, are based on student feedback. There are more examples and diagrams to illustrate and summarize certain models and principles of biology. Adequate text has been added so that this manual now reads more like a textbook rather than previous editions, which contained several schematic outlines. Chapters 19 and 20, on Digestion and Respiration, have been completely re-written and include several illustrations. The student who utilizes the new and improved version of **Almost Painless Biology** will no longer need to acquire another biology book as an ancillary to comprehend the doctrines of biology. This edition, along with the pre-recorded video lectures which are available on-line, should suffice in the study of introductory biology.

Video Recordings

The lectures were recorded live during class as well as in the professional recording studio at St. Thomas University. Mr. Carlos DeYarza, Multimedia Coordinator for the Office of Information Technology, subsequently edited them. They are available to all students who enroll in General Biology for non-majors and are synchronized with the chapters of the new edition of **Almost Painless Biology**.

Dedication

I dedicate this manual to BJA whose constant support and encouragement have guided me through countless projects and endeavors and to whom I am forever grateful.

About the Author

John Abdirkin, MD

Professor of Biology

Program Director for the School of Science, Technology and Engineering Management

Coordinator of the "2 +2" St. Thomas University / University of Miami Joint BSN Nursing Program

St. Thomas University, Miami, Florida

Dr. John Abdirkin earned his Medical Degree at the University of Bologna, School of Medicine and Surgery in Bologna, Italy. He joined the faculty of St. Thomas University in 1996 and in 2005 advanced to the rank of Full Professor of Biology. To date, he is the only member of the Biology Department at St. Thomas to have achieved this prestigious scholastic level. Dr. Abdirkin teaches Anatomy, Physiology, Biology, and Medical Terminology to Pre-Med and Nursing students as well as courses in Bioregions and General Biology for non-science majors.

UNIVERSITY ADVANCEMENT: Dr. Abdirkin coordinates the "2 +2" Joint Nursing Program with the University of Miami which has been completely restructured and reorganized to meet the high academic standards required to transition to UM. Furthermore, he played a key role in acquiring a $1.75 million endowment, which provides enough scholarships annually to allow 15 to 20 qualified nursing students the opportunity to attend STU tuition-free.

AUTHOR: Dr. Abdirkin has published two instructional manuals, entitled: ***Almost Painless Biology*** and ***Chemistry with Ease***. These manuals are designed, as "user-friendly" tools to assist students in the learning process by breaking down complex concepts into easily understood segments. He has authored articles in ***Vital Signs*** magazine and in ***South Florida Hospital News*** on nursing educational partnerships.

TECHNOLOGY: Dr. Abdirkin is particularly interested in on-line instruction, interactive education and state-of-the-art information on technology standards and tools to enhance educational programs. He has integrated video recorded modules from his own lectures with interactive media into the curriculum of General Biology as an innovative method to communicate, reinforce and expand the course content of the program.

RESEARCH AND SCHOLARLY INTERESTS: During his tenure at STU, Dr. Abdirkin has been involved in a myriad of projects. Recently, Dr. Abdirkin took part in the **Summer Research Internship Program (SRI)** in which he incorporated high fidelity simulation (SimMan) in developing the curriculum of the first course in cybernetic training at STU. This program teaches students how to conduct medical examinations by practicing the techniques and skills involved in a proper physical assessment. A virtual simulation suite was designed and built to look exactly like a technologically advanced hospital suite. Dr. Abdirkin has explored student retention and achievement to support faculty while he was involved with the **Title V Transformational Leadership Grant**. He was a participant in the **College Cost Reduction and Access Grant for Hispanic Serving Institutions (CCRA)** to ensure that biology course descriptions accurately coincide with the Florida State numbering system. Dr. Abdirkin conducted sponsored research for the **Miami-Dade County Mayor's Initiative on Aging** which was an exploratory, community-based study to determine the effect of a multifaceted health promotion program on older individuals. He was an investigator for the **NIH-funded Granny Grant**, which assessed the mental health status of minority caretaker grandparents. Since Dr. Abdirkin is experienced in curriculum development, he became involved with **Project Success**, to improve the conditions of learning and instruction of limited English proficient (LEP) students in Miami-Dade Public Schools. He also co-authored the **FIPSE** and **NASA** Grants, which provided computerized assemblages and data acquisition systems for the Physiology Laboratory allowing students to conduct medical-school level exercises.

COMMITTEES: Dr. Abdirkin is a member of the *Rank, Compensation and Welfare Committee*, the *Admissions Review Committee for Undergraduate Enrollment*, the *Nursing Scholarship Disbursement Committee*, the *St. Thomas University Scholarship Committee*, and the *Financial Aid Appeals Committee*.

COMMUNITY: Dr. Abdirkin routinely assists in community fund raising activities for organizations including **Children's Diagnostic and Treatment Center** (North Broward Hospital District).

INTERESTS: Dr. Abdirkin has traveled extensively to all parts of Europe, Israel, China, Indonesia, Canada, the Caribbean Islands, Mexico, South America, the Scandinavian Countries, and Russia.

Introduction

Natural Sciences

The science which is concerned with objects or processes observable in nature is called Natural Science. The Natural Sciences include both the Life Sciences and the Physical Sciences. Biology is a Life Science and there are many different fields of biology (Microbiology, Anatomy, Zoology etc.). If you study the chemical reactions in living organisms, this would combine both biology and chemistry. Therefore, this would be considered **Biochemistry**.

- The science of objects or processes observable in nature. The Natural sciences include:

Life Sciences

    – study of living organisms

Physical Science

    – study of natural laws other than those of living things

    – non-living objects

Biology:

a) Microbiology
b) Bacteriology
c) Parasitology
d) Virology
e) Fungi
f) Zoology
g) Botany
h) Molecular Biology
i) Cell Biology
j) Histology
k) Genetics
l) Evolution
m) Ecology
n) Physiology (function)—neurophysiology, exercise physiology, etc...

Examples of Physical Sciences:

a) Physics
b) Chemistry
c) Astronomy
d) Geology
e) Meteorology

    o) Anatomy (structure)—microscopic, surface, gross, etc...

    p) Embryology

    q) Immunology

    r) Marine Biology

Biology

Biology ≡ The Scientific study of life and all its forms, from ancestral species of 4 billion years ago to contemporary organisms. It includes the life "processes" of living beings such as:

nutrition (eating)	circulation (blood)
digestion (absorption of nutrients)	reproduction (continuation of species)
growth (development and repair)	regulation (nervous and hormonal)
respiration (breathing)	defense (immune system)

Biodiversity

5 - 30 million different species have been estimated. There are 5 Kingdoms: **Monera** (bacteria), **Protists** (paramecium and amoeba), **Fungi** (mushrooms and yeast), **Plants** and **Animals** (fish, amphibians, reptiles, birds and mammals).

Only 1.5 million named:

260,000 plants, 500,000 vertebrates, 750,000 insects

Tropical Rain Forest (Africa, Asia, Central & South America.)

greatest amount of life

half the earth's species reside in tropical rainforests

showplace for Mother Nature

canopy—dense foliage at high altitude. It is difficult to study the canopy (100 feet above ground) however, it is possible to climb the trees to do research or land on the canopy using a helium balloon which carries a tree-top raft. The scientists bounce around on this strong net to collect their specimens. It is in the canopy of a tropical rainforest where most species reside.

DeForestation

This is the practice or abuse of chopping down trees in a rainforest for lumber or fuel without replanting new trees. As a result, many species no longer have a habitat in which to survive. It could lead to their extinction.

SCORE:

A. Number incorrect answers = _____

B. 25 - (A) = _____ (subtract to get number of correct answers)

C. Take B (number of correct answers) and multiply by 4 = _____ (grade out of 100%)

PRE TEST

Please circle the choice (a, b c, or d) that you believe is the best answer for each question. Do not begin this Pre-test until we meet on the first day of class when additional instructions will be given.

1. We have <u>day and night</u> because:

    a) the sun goes around the earth

    b) the moon goes around the earth

    c) the earth goes around the sun

    d) the earth spins on its axis

2. We can use the sun to tell time because at <u>12:00 noon</u>, the sun is:

    a) in the eastern sky

    b) in the western sky

    c) in the southern sky

    d) directly overhead (straight up)

3. It takes about one _____ for the <u>moon</u> to go around <u>the earth one time</u>.

    a) hour

    b) day

    c) month

    d) year

4. Venus, Mars, and Jupiter are planets. We can often see them at night:

    a) but only after midnight

    b) but only with a telescope (or a pair of binoculars)

    c) because every night they are in the same place in the sky

    d) because they are often brighter than the brightest star

5. If a crystal can scratch glass, then:

    a) it <u>is</u> a diamond

    b) it <u>is not</u> a diamond

    c) it <u>may be</u> a diamond

    d) it <u>probably is not</u> a diamond

6. The dinosaurs:

    a) lived long before cave-men

    b) lived at the same time as cave-men

    c) are still living someplace on earth

    d) never lived anywhere on earth

7. Plants get their food:

    a) from the soil in which they are planted

    b) from the water which wets their roots and leaves

    c) through the process of photosynthesis

    d) through the process of transpiration

8. The blood flowing through human veins (as opposed to human arteries) is:

    a) bright red (the same color as in the arteries)

    b) dark red (darker than in the arteries)

    c) blue

    d) clear

9. Observe the object pictured above. How would you calculate its <u>volume</u>?

    a) Use the formula: Length x Width x Height

    b) Use the formula: 6(Length x Width x Height)

    c) Use the formula: Length + Width + Height

    d) Use the formula: 2(Length x Width) + 2(Width x Height) + 2(Length x Height)

10. Iron combines with oxygen to form rust. One should therefore find that rust (such as from a rusty nail) weighs:

   a) the <u>same</u> as the iron that it came from

   b) <u>less</u> than the iron it came from

   c) <u>more</u> than the iron it came from

   d) <u>could be more or less</u> than the iron it came from

11. When several Amino Acids are linked together, they may form:

   a) sugars

   b) carbohydrates

   c) alpha hydrates

   d) proteins

12. The study of how organisms interact with each other and their physical environment is called:

   a) population integration

   b) symbiosis

   c) ecology

   d) mutual predation

13. A type of agriculture whereby trees are cut and burned releasing nutrients into the soil, then the soil is farmed for a few years and then cut and burned again is called:

   a) repetitive farming

   b) slash and burn

   c) monoculture

   d) competitive exclusion

14. The Density of an object is determined by:

   a) the Mass of the object multiplied by its Volume

   b) the Mass of the object divided by its Volume

   c) the Surface area of the object

   d) the Weight of the object

15. Energy that is not used up because it is virtually inexhaustible is called:

   a) non-renewable energy

   b) renewable energy

   c) resident energy

   d) limited energy

16. Water falling to the ground as rain, sleet, snow or hail is called:

    a) discharge

    b) transpiration

    c) precipitation

    d) evaporation

17. When water vapor (gas) is cooled down to become liquid water, the process is called:

    a) evaporation

    b) boiling

    c) condensation

    d) melting

18. Which of the following properties of water is true?

    a) few substances can dissolve in water

    b) water absorbs very little heat

    c) water boils at 100 degrees Centigrade

    d) water becomes ice at 50 degrees Centigrade

19. The death of an entire group of organisms from the earth is called:

    a) extermination

    b) endangerment

    c) extirpation

    d) extinction

20. Hormones used by males and females to attract opposite sex are called:

    a) intrinsicones

    b) chlorinated hydrocarbons

    c) phermones

    d) body fluids

21. If you subtract 1,250 from 2,020 you will get:

    a) 3270

    b) -770

    c) 770

    d) 1.62

22. The square root of 81 is:

    a) cannot be determined without a calculator

    b) 8

    c) 9

    d) 40.5

23. What is the most common litter found along beaches?

    a) aluminum

    b) plastic

    c) paper

    d) animal excrement

24. A group of highly toxic substances that can be formed during incineration is:

    a) methane

    b) leachate

    c) dioxin

    d) Bhopal

25. In the early twentieth century, the most widely held environmentalist position was _____ in which the federal government took an active role in protecting forests and other natural resources.

    a) transcendentalism

    b) conservatism

    c) progressionism

    d) sustainable development

Review Questions

i. What is the difference between the Life Sciences and the Physical Sciences?

ii. What would a Histologist study?

iii. Explain what is meant by "the continuation of a species"?

iv. What does Biodiversity signify?

v. What are the Natural Laws?

Organization of Nature: Chemical, Biological, and Ecological

Organization of Nature

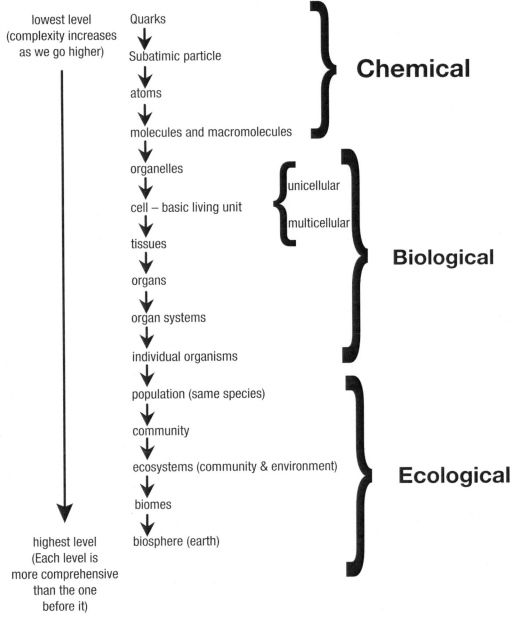

lowest level
(complexity increases
as we go higher)

Quarks
↓
Subatimic particle
↓
atoms
↓
molecules and macromolecules

} **Chemical**

organelles
↓
cell – basic living unit

{ unicellular

multicellular

↓
tissues
↓
organs
↓
organ systems
↓
individual organisms

} **Biological**

population (same species)
↓
community
↓
ecosystems (community & environment)
↓
biomes
↓
biosphere (earth)

} **Ecological**

highest level
(Each level is
more comprehensive
than the one
before it)

Ecology – how living organisms interact with each other and the environment.

The Levels of Organization

Nature is organized in various levels. There are **chemical levels, biological levels and ecological levels** (see page 1 of APB). We will start with the subatomic particles and move up the hierarchy until we reach the organism, then continue with the ecological levels, eventually leading to the Biosphere. As we go higher and higher, the levels become more and more complex. Each level is built from the components of the previous one.

The **subatomic particles**; protons, neutrons and electrons are the smallest part of an **atom**. The **protons** and **neutrons** are in the nucleus of the atom (atomic nucleus), which is the core of an atom and the electrons circle in orbits around the nucleus. Therefore, an atom is made up of these three components (see page 4 for the structure of an atom). Protons are positively charged and neutrons have no charge. **Electrons** are negatively charged and they are also the lightest subatomic particle. The positive and negative forces of the protons and electrons create attractions (opposite attract), which actually hold the atom together or intact. The electrons orbit around the atom at a certain distance from the nucleus.

Atoms are the basic unit of **elements**. An element is a substance, which cannot be broken down by chemical means or converted to another substance. The number of protons an atom contains determines which atom it is and is defined as the **atomic number**. Each atom in a particular element has the same atomic number. For example, every carbon atom has 6 protons or an atomic number of 6. Some other examples of atoms are the hydrogen atom or the oxygen atom. All the symbols on the Periodic Table represent all of the atoms (elements) known to man. H means hydrogen, O stands for oxygen, Cu is used for copper, etc...

Atoms combine to form **molecules or compounds**. A compound is made up of two or more elements, which are in *definite and fixed proportions*. For example, water is H_2O. There are always two hydrogen atoms to one oxygen atom in water. That is, the proportion is always 2 to 1 (2:1). The atoms of water are *chemically bonded* together which means that certain electrons of the oxygen atom and the electrons of the two hydrogen atoms interact with one another in such a fashion that they become a part of each other's orbits (electron sharing = **covalent bond**). The electrons, which are shared, enable their atoms to form the compound called water. When atoms combine to form compounds (or molecules), only the electrons in the outer most energy level or shell interact to form the bond that exists between them.

Water is a compound, which has properties that are different than either the hydrogen or the oxygen atoms that it is made from. Or we can say that new properties **emerge** when these atoms combine to form the compound water. Hydrogen and oxygen are gases and they are **homo-nuclear diatomic** molecules. When they combine, the compound that forms is a liquid. Water has its own unique characteristics for example, it freezes at 0°C and boils at 100°C. Water is the most abundant molecule in a cell.

$$2H_2 + O_2 \rightarrow 2H_2O$$

Other examples of molecules are sugars, amino acids and fatty acids.

Molecules make up larger molecules called **macromolecules** (see macromolecules on pages 5-7 of APB). Some examples of macromolecules are carbohydrates, proteins and lipids.

Macromolecules make up the little organs that we find inside of a cell and they are called **organelles**. Each organelle carries out a certain function. For example, the mitochondrion is responsible for cellular respiration.

If one considers all of the organelles together, plus the **cytoplasm** and the **cell membrane**, then we arrive at the **cell** which is the smallest unit that can survive and reproduce on its own. **Single-celled organisms** (unicellular) are only one cell large but can live freely and independently. Some examples of single celled organisms are the amoeba and the paramecium. There are also **multicellular organisms** in which there are groups of specialized cells that are organized to perform specific functions (see types of cells: APB, page 8). Humans are an example of a multicellular organism. We are made up of trillions of cells.

Tissues are groups of cells that function together. There are four types of tissues: **epithelial**, **connective**, **muscle**, and **nerve**.

When two or more tissues combine in a certain pattern to perform a particular task we arrive at the next level of organization, called the **organ**. For example, the stomach is an organ made up of epithelial, connective, muscle, and nerve tissue. So all four tissues are represented in the stomach.

When two or more organs interact for a purpose they make up an **organ system**. For example, the stomach, esophagus, small intestine, and large intestine, all make up the digestive system. (See page 9)

When one considers all of the organ systems together, we arrive at the **individual organism**.

A group of individuals that are of the same species which breed with one another and live in the same area is called a **population**.

Several different populations in an area make up a **community**. Therefore, a community consists of all the different populations, which interact and coexist in a particular area. These interactions include:

1. **Competition** for resources - when two or more species attempt to use the same limited resources each species is harmed since access to resources is reduced for both.

2. **Predation** by predators -one species is benefitted; the other is harmed (predators kill their prey)

3. **Symbiosis** - intimate, prolonged interaction, between different species: one species benefits, but the second species may be a) unaffected, b) harmed or c) helped by the relationship:

    a) **commensalism** - one species is benefitted but the other is neither helped nor harmed

    b) **parasitism** - one species is harmed. A parasite feeds on the host without killing the host.

    c) **mutualism** - both species benefit.

When you consider the community plus the physical environment (water, soil, air, temperature, light, etc.) we talk about an **ecosystem**.

Several ecosystems make up a **biome.** Biomes are large regions which are defined by their vegetation (based on climate) and certain species of animals that live off of this vegetation. The biomes are divided into those on land (desserts, rainforests, etc.), which are called the **terrestrial biomes.** There are large areas with similar environmental conditions and characteristic plant life. In fact, they are defined and named for their vegetation. Those with water are the **aquatic biomes**, like the oceans or the rivers. Therefore, biomes are large regions made up of several ecosystems which have a certain type of vegetation and animal population.

Tropical Rainforests (Wetlands) are an example of terrestrial biomes:

They are near the equator (South America, Africa and Southeast Asia) at 80 degrees latitude. The rainfall is greater than 100 inches/year and there is little seasonal variation.

You find huge evergreen trees in tropical rainforests with the highest biodiversity of any ecosystem. The rainforests only cover 6% of the total land on earth - but they account for over 50% of the world's species. The vegetation is layered (stratified): At 150 feet are the tallest trees called the **emergents**, next are the trees at 100 feet which make up the canopy, and then come the shorter trees. There is the hardly any edible plant material close to ground since the nutrients are in the vegetation. Therefore, life is arboreal, the soil is infertile and is not good for agriculture if the trees are cut down and used for lumber.

Human Impact on Rainforests - The trees are taken for lumber (deforestation) or the land is cleared for ranching. As a result, the rainfall decreases in deforested areas (since a lot of rain comes from the water that evaporates from the leaves). Eventually the soil becomes bricklike and impenetrable and, there will also be a loss of medicines and species. 50% of the rainforests have already been destroyed. The goal now is to achieve sustainable forests (or to derive benefits from the forests by tourism and sustainable harvesting).

When one considers all of the biomes in the world we arrive at the **biosphere**. Planet earth with all of its organisms, lands, seas, rivers, and the atmosphere, etc. make up the biosphere.

Structure of an Atom

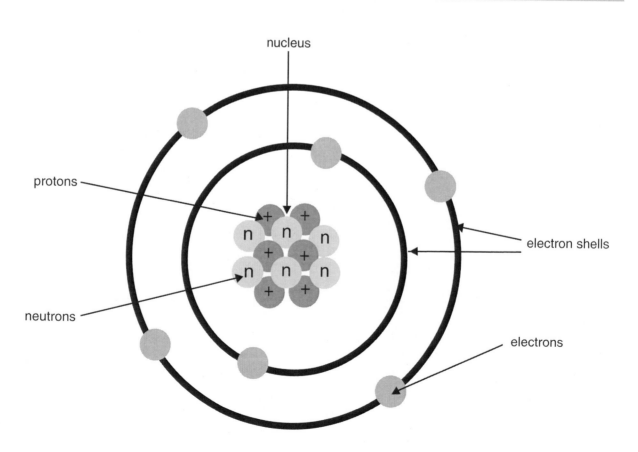

Atoms, Molecules and Biological Molecules

Atoms are the basic structural units of matter. Two or more atoms may combine to form molecules (like water, H_2O, or sugars, $C_6H_{12}O_6$). The larger molecules are made up of several smaller molecules (monomers) and they are called macromolecules for example; many sugars (molecules), like glucose, are linked together to form carbohydrates (macromolecule). Many amino acids connected to each other form proteins, fatty acids make up lipids and nucleic acids (DNA and RNA) are made from nucleotides. Therefore, the most important biological molecules are carbohydrates, proteins, lipids and nucleic acids.

The carbohydrates, proteins and lipids are formed from their respective monomers, which combine or bond together as a result of a **dehydration synthesis** reaction. That is, a water molecule is removed between every pair of monomers so that a bond forms which will hold the two adjacent monomers together. The two monomers line up next to each other, and, a hydrogen (H) from one monomer binds with a **hydroxyl group** (OH) of the other monomer. Therefore, the H and OH are removed and water is formed. The parts dangling now from each monomer side connect to form a covalent bond, which holds them together.

Macromolecules

I. Sugars make up Carbohydrates

> **Sugars:** consist of carbons and hydrogens
>> examples: glucose, fructose, ribose... these are **Monosaccharides**
>> general formula: CnH_2nOn (n = the number of carbons)
>
>> glucose: $C_6H_{12}O_6$

β—glucose

maltose

> **Disaccharides:** double sugars:
>> maltose, sucrose

> **Polysaccharides:** many sugars:
>> starch, cellulose, glycogen

***Function of carbohydrates*—they provide energy and are the main source of energy for all living organisms.**

Carbohydrates (Size)	Name	Examples	Function
One sugar molecule	**Monosaccharide** (simple sugars)	Glucose (made in the chloroplasts of plant cells), fructose, and ribose	-Fuel cellular activities -Form larger carbohydrates
Two sugar molecules	**Disaccharide**	Sucrose and lactose	-Short term energy storage -If cell needs energy, these are broken down to monosaccharides
Three or more	**Polysaccharide**	Starch (roots), glyocen (liver & muscle), chitin (makes up body covering of insects, spiders, crabs, and lobsters), cellulose (plants-tree trunks and is also a dietary fiber)	-Long term energy storage -Used to make structural molecules that give support (chitin and cellulose)

II. Amino acids make up Proteins

Some amino acids are: alanine, arginine, methionine, glycine, trytophane

General Formula: (amino group) NH_2 –Ⓒ– COOH (carboxyl group)

with H above the C and R below the C (variable group-there are 20 different R groups)

Dipeptide: two (2) amino acids linked together

Polypeptide: many amino acids bonded together

Protein: greater than 50 amino acids; Proteins are made up of the 20 different amino acids that exist. The sequence or order of amino acids in a protein determines the type of protein formed and its properties. As such proteins have many functions.

Function of proteins—**defense (immunoglobulins), may guide the chemical reactions of metabolic processes (enzymes), act as chemical messengers that travel in the blood (hormones- like insulin or testosterone), provide structural support, transport other molecules like oxygen (for example, hemoglobin in RBC), some even have a contractile property (found in muscles, like actin) and they also can provide energy.**

III. Fatty acids make up Lipids

Fatty acid:

$$R - \overset{\overset{\displaystyle O}{\|}}{C} - OH$$

(The R group represents a long chain of Carbons and Hydrogens)

Types of Lipids:

TRG—triglycerides

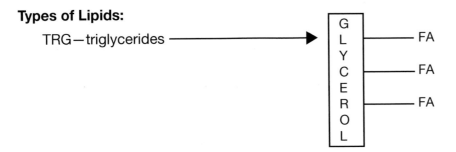

Steroids

Sex hormones

Phospholipids—found in membranes

Function of lipids—**structure of membranes and long-term energy storage.** In fact, they are more efficient than carbohydrates as an energy source since they weigh less.

To form a **phospholipid**, one of the fatty acids (FA) from the TRG above is replaced with a phosphate group - PO_4.

Lipids have large regions, which contain several carbons and hydrogens. These are non-polar areas so they do not like water. We say that this area is **hydrophobic** and it makes lipids insoluble in water.

Types of Cells

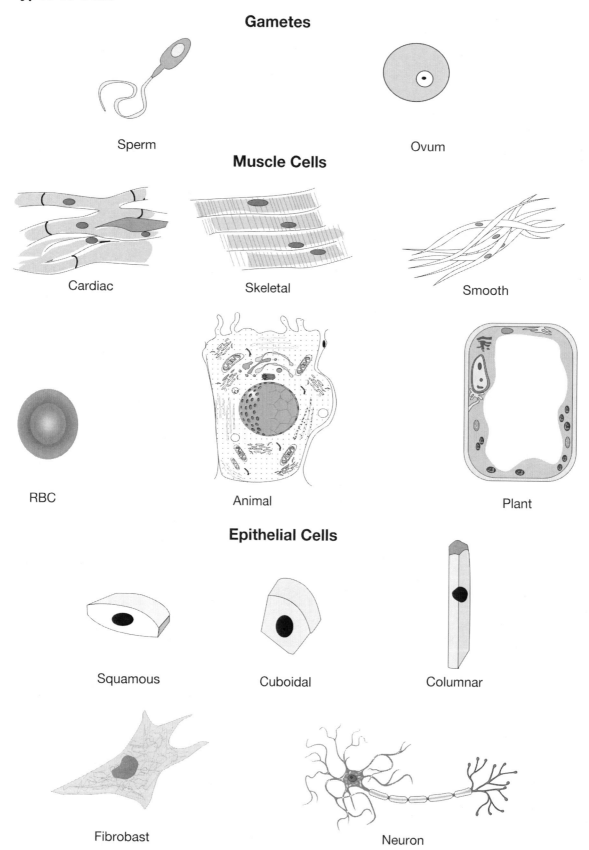

Gametes

Sperm

Ovum

Muscle Cells

Cardiac

Skeletal

Smooth

RBC

Animal

Plant

Epithelial Cells

Squamous

Cuboidal

Columnar

Fibrobast

Neuron

Organ Systems

Organ System	Function	Component Organs
• **Respiratory**		
• **Integumentary**		The skin is an organ. When you add in the hair, nails and glands, you now have what is called the integumentary system.
• **Skeletal**		
• **Muscular**		Each muscle of the body is considered an organ. All of the muscles together make up the skeletal muscle system.
• **Endocrine**		
• **Nervous**		
• **Digestive**		
• **Circulatory**		
• **Lymphatic**		
• **Immune***		
• **Urinary**		
• **Reproductive**		

* The immune system has to be able to distinguish between its own antigens (self) and those of a foreign body (non-self).

_____

Last Name, First Name

General Biology
Dr. Abdirkin

Review Questions

1. Distinguish among atoms and molecules.

2. Discuss the function of three of the four principle types of biological macromolecules.

3. Define ecological community and list three important types of community interactions.

4. Explain two undesirable affects of agriculture in the tropical rainforest biome.

5. Starting with the subatomic particles, list all the levels of organization (chemical, biological, and ecological) in order up to the biosphere.

Photosynthesis: Producers and Consumers

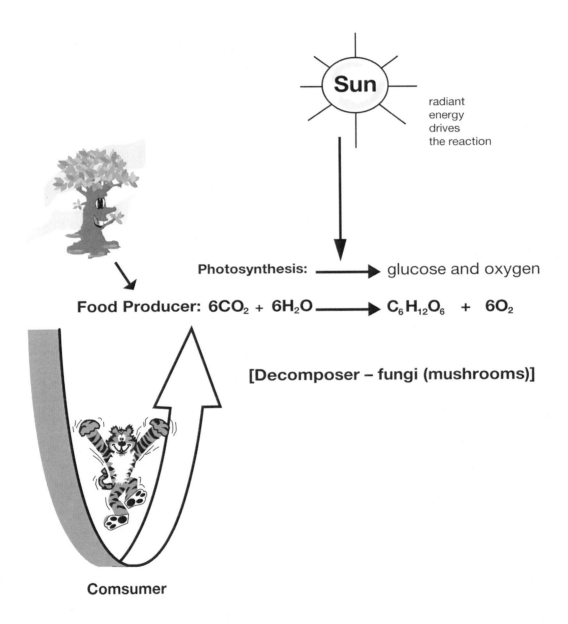

radiant
energy
drives
the reaction

Photosynthesis: ⟶ glucose and oxygen

Food Producer: $6CO_2 + 6H_2O \longrightarrow C_6H_{12}O_6 + 6O_2$

[Decomposer – fungi (mushrooms)]

Comsumer

The consumers eat the producers. When consumers or producers die, their remains are recycled back into the soil by the decomposers. Therefore, the plants get to use these monomers in their cells to build the molecules it needs.

The Interdependency amongst Living Organisms

Ecology is the study of how living organisms interact with each other and the environment. For example, the radiant energy from the sun is captured by plants which use this energy in a process called **photosynthesis** to form glucose and oxygen. Plants are what we call **food producers**. Animals which feed on plants either directly or indirectly are called **consumers**.

If a cow eats some grass and then we eat the cow, the cow is what we call the **primary consumer** and we are the **secondary consumer**.

If a zebra eats grass, it gets the energy **directly.** A lion that eats the zebra would get the energy **indirectly.**

There are also **decomposers** (in addition to producers and consumers). A decomposer feeds on the remains of other dead organisms, breaking the substances down to raw materials which are then recycled back to the producers. An example of a decomposer is a mushroom (funghi).

Biology is the study of living organisms and how they operate and relate to one another.

Photosynthesis

Plants sustain life by providing oxygen which is used by other organisms (for breathing) and they also produce fuel (for energy and growth) in the form of glucose.

In the presence of **light energy** from the sun:

Water   +   Carbon dioxide ⟶ Oxygen   +   Glucose

                                     (waste product (chemical
                                     released into energy)
                                     the
                                     atmosphere)

Photosynthetic Organisms

    Plants, Algae (cyanobacteria), and some Prokaryotes

Pigments

    a) Pigments are substances that have a color due to selective absorption. They are chemical compounds, which reflect only certain wavelengths of visible light. They take on the appearance of the colors that these wavelengths represent. For example, if a pigment reflects purple light then this pigment is the color purple. But more importantly is the ability of pigments to absorb certain wavelengths because this is energy that biological organisms can use. In plants, algae, and cyanobacteria, pigments are the means by which the energy of the sunlight is captured for photosynthesis. However, since each pigment reacts with only a narrow range of the spectrum, there is usually the need to produce several kinds of pigments, each of a different color, to capture more of the sun's energy.

    b) **chlorophyll a**: absorbs violet, blue and red wavelengths. These are the wavelengths used in the process of photosynthesis as energy to propel the reactions. As a result, solar energy is converted in the process to chemical energy which is stored in glucose. Chlorophyll a takes on the appearance of the reflected color, which is green.

    c) **chlorophyll b**: this is also green for the same reason

    d) **carotenoids**: orange and yellow are not absorbed

Chloroplast: organelle in which photosynthesis takes place. The light reactions of photosynthesis are carried out on the **thylakoid membranes** and the dark reactions in the **stroma**:

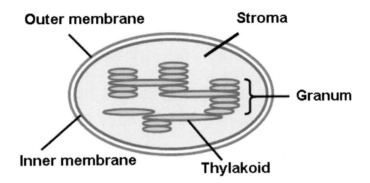

Chemical Reactions of Photosynthesis:

    1. The Light Reactions (thylakoid membranes)

        Light energy + water → oxygen + ATP + NADPH

        Production of ATP and NADPH which are chemical molecules, each containing the energy that will be used in the dark reactions.

    2. **The Dark Reactions (stroma)**

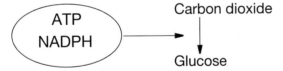

        The energy (ATP and NADPH) produced in the light reactions propels the dark reactions which produce glucose from carbon dioxide.

Importance of Glucose:

    • It is a major source of energy for most of the functions all organisms must carry out.

    • Primary source of energy for the brain

Earth's First Atmosphere

The first atmosphere on earth (around 4 billion years ago) only contained nitrogen, carbon-dioxide and water for the most part. When the first primitive microorganisms like bacteria and algae (ancestors of plants) began to use the carbon dioxide and water to produce glucose, oxygen was the product. With the availability of oxygen, more advanced organisms evolved and used it (along with glucose) to produce energy.

In fact, the reverse reaction of photosynthesis is called **cellular respiration**. The by-products, carbon dioxide and water, are the components plants need. Animals and plants need each other to produce energy.

$$\text{cellular respiration: } C_6H_{12}O_6 + 6O_2 \rightarrow 6CO_2 + 6H_2O$$

Leaves and Stomata

The **Stoma** (plural **stomata**) is a pore, found in the leaf and stem epidermis that is used for gas exchange. The pore is bordered by a pair of specialized cells known as **guard cells** that are responsible for regulating the size of the opening. Air, containing carbon dioxide enters the plant through these openings so it may be used in photosynthesis. Oxygen produced by photosynthesis in the leaf interior exits through these same openings. Also, water vapor is released into the atmosphere through these pores in a process called **transpiration**.

_____

Last Name, First Name

General Biology
Dr. Abdirkin

Exercises

1. Plants are autotrophs since they make their own food by photosynthesis. What are the consumers called?

2. What are some examples of decomposers?

3. Suppose there is an energy source which emits blue, green and yellow light. If a yellow pigment is available, which wavelengths of light can it absorb? What color will this pigment be to an observer?

4. Why are ATP and NADPH important in photosynthesis?

5. Explain the significance of stomata.

Scientific Method

3

The Scientific Method

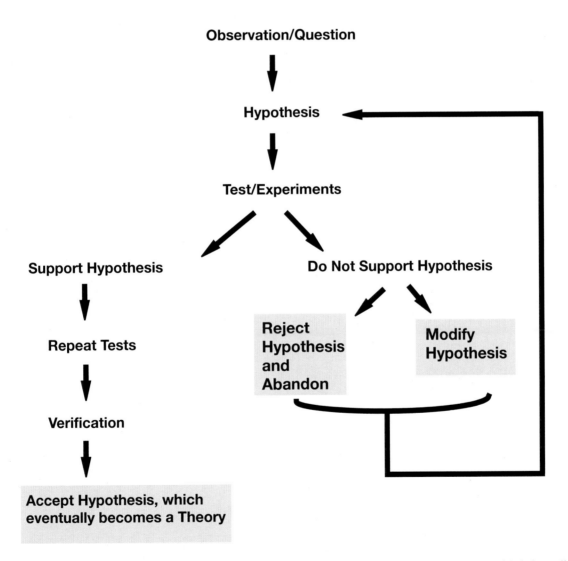

After an explanation is proposed to answer a question about some phenomenon, which is called the **hypothesis**, one can usually make a **prediction**. Then of course, the hypothesis has to be tested with **experiments** over and over again. This is called **reproducibility** or the results from experimentation must be able to be reproduced.

Application of the scientific method:

You are late to an appointment and are rushing. You get to your car and:

OBSERVE - the car will not start

QUESTION - why doesn't my car start?

HYPOTHESIS - "maybe the battery is dead"

PREDICTION - if the battery is dead, then a new battery should start my car

EXPERIMENT - take the battery from my friend's brand new car and put it into my car. RESULT of EXPERIMENT - car starts

CONCLUSION - the battery was dead, so my hypothesis is correct!

Designing an Experiment: Control Group and Variables

When designing an experiment, a **control group** is often incorporated which serves as the standard or reference to which the **experimental group** is compared. The control group in a drug study for example, would not test the new drug. The individuals in this group would receive a **placebo** (sugar pill), which would not have any pharmacological effects on the physiology of the organism. The experimental group on the other hand, gets to test the new drug to see what happens.

In addition, an experiment is well designed if there is only one variable or one item, which is varied so that we can observe its effect without a complicated situation occurring that would otherwise cloud the picture. There are two types of variables: the **dependent variable** is the observed result of something else that is manipulated. It will change, as it depends on other factors and we can measure this change. The **independent variable** is the value being manipulated.

For example, Vitamin C intake (independent variable) or the amount of Vitamin C one consumes will influence life expectancy (dependent variable). The amount of Vitamin C is going to be manipulated or varied to see what its effect is on life expectancy, which is what we want to measure.

Law of Falling Bodies

Observation:	Many objects fall
Hypothesis: (first)	"Objects fall at different rates" (i.e: heavier objects fall faster)
Experiment:	Drop stones of various weights from the same height. These stones do not vary in weight very much from one another.

Experimental Results

All the stones hit the ground at the same time (because there is very little difference in their weights)

New Hypothesis: (second)

"All bodies fall to earth at the same rate independent of their weight"

Reproduce Experiment:

Drop more objects. Now we use objects that vary greatly in weight. For example, a boulder and a feather.

Experimental Results:

Most of these objects obey the new hypothesis however, paper and feathers drop much more slowly than heavier objects.

Modify New Hypothesis: (third)

We must include the effects of air resistance. "In the absence of air resistance (i.e. vacuum) all bodies fall to earth at same rate". The friction of the air must be considered. A boulder will overcome air resistance a lot faster than a feather. But if we remove air resistance and conduct the experiment in a vacuum, all objects fall at the same rate.

Reproduce Experiments:

We always get the same results therefore, this became a Theory.

The Scientific Method

1. **Observation**
2. **Hypothesis**
3. **Experiment/Test**
4. **Repeat**
5. **Accept** or **Reject**
   ↓
   Theory

Example of Scientific Method

(1962) **Kinky Hair Syndrome**—Menkes Disease: Menke observed that in one out of every one thousand births, some newborns present the following:

Symptoms—lethargy, yellow skin

hair: no color (white)

stands on end

breaks off

"stubby" appearance

1. Menke **observed** that the hair of these babies is like that of a peculiar wool, found on sheep that graze from a soil the lacks copper.

2. **Hypothesis**—since their hair (babies) resembles this wool, then they should also have a copper deficiency.

3. **Experiments** were designed to test this idea...

    Results: These neonates were getting copper in their diet however, the copper stays in the intestinal cells so it cannot get into the blood.

    Without copper, the hair is not constructed properly so it falls apart.

4. **Repeat tests to verify**

    Therefore, Kinky Hair Syndrome is due to a copper deficiency (but not because it is deficient in the diet, but rather because it cannot be absorbed by the intestinal cells)

Last Name, First Name

Exercises

1. An experiment is designed to test a drug that reduces anxiety. However, some members of the control group claim that they are less anxious after taking the placebo. What does this illustrate?

2. An experiment is designed to test the effects of a new plant fertilizer. Some bean plants are grown with the full dose of the recommended amount of fertilizer. Another group of plants gets only 50% of that amount. A third group gets 25%. The length of stem growth is measured every 5 days in all the plants. What is the dependent variable? What is the independent variable?

3. Explain what air resistance is.

Features of Living Organisms

The Characteristics which define Life

Organisms: (living creatures) have the following features:

- constructed from **cells** (the basic living unit)
- highly **organized** (atoms → organism, recall the levels of organization)
- capture **energy** (directly or indirectly)

$\left.\begin{array}{c} \\ \\ \end{array}\right\}$ = Metabolism   for growth, development and reproduction

- obtain **nutrients**
- **respond** to environmental change (stimuli) = irritability
- traits—contained in genes and **passed on to offspring.** Therefore the organism's individual traits are inherited in the DNA.
- **evolve** and **adapt** by natural selection

"What is Life"?

1. Living organisms are organized from units called **cells**.
2. Living organisms are **highly organized** (see Levels of Organization page 1) from atoms to the individual organism.
3. Living organisms **capture and use energy** to carry out their **metabolic processes**.
4. Living organisms sense changes in the environment (stimuli) and respond to them. That is, they are **irritable**.
5. Living organisms are capable of **growing, developing, and reproducing** themselves.
6. The **genetic information** of an organism (DNA found in the chromosomes) which specifies its features and characteristics is passed on to its offspring.
7. Living organisms **evolve** and **adapt** to their environment by **natural selection**. The genes that express favorable traits which enable the organism to survive in the environment will be passed on to the next generation.

Cell Players

5

Galileo arranged two glass lenses in a cylinder and invented the first microscope.

Robert Hooke used his simple microscope to observe a piece of cork (from the bark of a tree). He saw small compartments that were lined with walls. He was observing dead plant cells. He also saw the "juices" inside of a cell called the cytoplasm as well as the thick plant cell wall.

Anthony Van Leeuwenhoek improved the earlier microscopes and observed moving microorganisms which he called "animalcules." Actually, he was observing protozoa, bacteria, and sperm cells.

Robert Brown with an even better lens was able to sharpen the focus and observe a dark spot in the center of the cell which turned out to be the nucleus.

Schwann said that both animals (which lack cell walls) and plants are made up of cells. And these cells have an individual life of their own even though they are part of a whole organism.

Virchow studied cell growth and reproduction. He concluded that every cell comes from a preexisting cell.

Date	Country	Player	Contribution
Early 1600s	Italy	**Galileo**	simplest microscope
Middle 1650s	England	**Hooke**	dead plant cells with juices
Late 1600s	Holland	**Leeuwenhoek**	improved microscope "animalcules": protozoa, bacteria, sperm
1820s		**Brown**	better lens, sharper focus, nucleus
1839		**Schwann**	animals lack cell wall cell: basic living unit
1849		**Virchow**	cell grows and reproduces, every cell comes from preexisting cell

The Cell Theory

1. All organisms are made up of one (**unicellular organism**) or more cells (**multicellular organism**).

2. The cell is the basic unit of life. It is the smallest entity that can be called **living**.

3. New cells only arise from **preexisting** ones by cell division.

Evolution and Geological Time Scale

6

Fossils = remains of extinct organisms. They are the evidence which supports Darwin's theory of evolution. Fossils give us a great deal of information:

- chronicle the evolution of a species

- used to trace the ancestry of a species

- give evidence of the relationships between different species

- provide clues about a species

- may be used to construct a skeleton

- indicate history about the environment

Introduction

All earth's inhabitants are related. Consider for example, a **tuna** fish and a **trout**. Obviously they both had a **fish-like ancestor**. Now compare a **tuna** (fish), **human** (mammal) and **frog** (amphibian). These are not the same types of animals however; they all had a common vertebrate ancestor whose species evolved and branched off, eventually giving rise to all three of them.

Evolution explains how all organisms, past and present, are related to one another. In fact, all life is connected and can be traced back to the **primeval prokaryotes**.

Evolution involves the changes that a species undergoes over time. Ancestral life forms evolved and branched off, eventually giving rise to all the different species. Therefore, all organisms are related.

1859: Darwin: *"On the origin of species by means of natural selection"* → Evolution is directed by **natural selection**. The individuals in a population have various **traits** (that differ amongst each individual). These traits are inherited. However, many organisms do not live to grow up and reproduce due to *"Survival of the Fittest"*: Certain traits are not advantageous for survival and reproduction, others are favorable. Environmental conditions are important to consider. Changes in the population accumulate and become adaptations for the particular species, enabling it to survive and reproduce.

The Concept of Survival of the Fittest

More organisms are produced than live to grow up and reproduce. A female fish lays thousands of eggs but only a certain percentage ever survives to reproductive age. There are **predators, diseases, and resources** which come into play. These factors reduce the number of survivors.

The Environment and Survival

Individuals with **short sparse hair** (i.e.: bears) may not survive a long, cold winter. But those (bears) with **longer and thicker hair** do because of the added insulation. In fact, they reproduce in the spring. So the **"trait"** thick hair is passed on to the next generation because it is a **favorable** trait. So populations that live in cold climates have **"adapted"** qualities which enable them to withstand the cold.

Evolution

- Explains the diversity of life on earth
- The earth is 4.5 billion years old
- Fossil evidence of prokaryotes (simplest single-celled organism, although they are capable of protein synthesis and cell respiration) suggest that life began in the water.

I. Fossil Formation

1. organism encased in sap that hardened

2. tissues frozen after death

3. sediments covered plants or animals

4. sedimentation also occurs in the water: the soft tissues decay and minerals replace teeth, shell or bone making solid casts

II. The Players

1. George Cuvier

Paleontology = study of fossils

Sedimentary rock forms layers

Succession of the different species in the layers over time

Catastrophism—natural disasters killed off the species in an area. For example, a volcano would erupt and the lava buried all the species. They became fossilized. New species moved in to repopulate the new habitat. They lived on top of those organisms that died off creating successive layers over time. Therefore, Cuvier spoke about catastrophes to explain the different species which appeared over time.

2. Jean Baptiste Lamark

Life evolved along with the earth

Organisms evolve new traits in response to their needs } This can

Beneficial qualities were passed on directly to their young } not occur!

If you work out and develop your muscles so they are well defined, this does not mean when you father a son he is born with bulky muscles.

3. Charles Lyell

Principles of Geology

Theory of **Uniformitianism** = shaping of the earth's features by a slow process. Lyell was not looking for such big events like Cuvier to explain how things changed. Rather, he said, that the earth's features change slowly by forces still in operation today. For example, the erosion that tides cause on a beach, windstorms, etc.

4. James Hutton

Described ancient earth

5. Charles Darwin

Galapagos Islands (1831): observed many odd species. There was a lot of variation in a small area

Hypothesis on evolution (1836). Small changes over a long period of time bring about great changes in a species

"On the Origin of Species by Natural Selection" - published in 1859. The evolution of a species was carried out by a process of nartural selection. This was not widely accepted at first!

6. Alfred Wallace (1858)

He had similar views as Darwin

7. Gregor Mendel

Principles of Heredity. He experimented with garden peas and observed flower traits. His principles of genetics explained what Darwin observed.

8. Thomas Hunt Morgan

Revealed the **Chromosomal Theory of Inheritance**

By understanding genetics it is possible to understand natural selection:

- reproduction → more organisms are born than the environment can support
- resources are limited
- competition for resources
- predation limits the number of surviving offspring
- individuals best **adapted** to their environment are able to obtain resources, survive and reproduce

Those traits that enhance survival become more common in the population (gene pool) and the genes that code for these traits are passed on to the next generation

III. Basics of Heredity

- the **gene** is the basic **unit of heredity**
- genes are distinct segments of **DNA**
- each strand of DNA is wound into a **chromosome**
- chromosomes are comprised of many different genes
- all chromosomes have the identical chemical make-up however, the difference is in the *sequence* of the **nucleic acids** in DNA

Genotype = genetic make-up. It determines the phenotype

Phenotype = visible, physical characteristics of offspring

Mutation = a change in the genetic sequence in a sperm or egg cell, which is then passed on to the offspring.

IV. Natural Selection

Note: Individuals do not evolve, populations of individuals do:

Natural selection works as environmental factors influence and interact with the variations found in the gene pool of the population. Certain traits give survival advantages, and over time the genes for these traits become more frequent in the population.

English Peppered Moth: Microevolution

	Light colored moth	**Dark colored moth**
Daytime (before industrial revolution) Moths rest on trees which are light colored	*blend* into the background, this is an *advantage*	easily spotted by birds so they do not survive and are *rare*
Industrial Revolution The environment changed, now the trees have become dark colored	become *rare*	this trait is now an *advantage,* so its frequency (genes) rises in the population

This example illustrates evolution even though no speciation occurred (a new species of moth did not evolve): the dark colored moths are still able to reproduce with the white colored ones and produce viable offspring. This illustrates the concept of **microevolution** (evolution on a small scale) since there have been changes in the frequency of the genes in a population's gene pool. Natural selection is the main and only source of microevolution. A population becomes better adapted to its environment. It is through **heritable variations** of any trait that natural selection is able to determine certain characteristics.

V. Fitness

Fitness is measured in **reproductive success**—the number of offspring. There is pressure on the individuals in a population not only to survive but also to find and attract a mate. Features that enhance sexual attractiveness (colorful plumage) may also be disadvantageous if this same trait attracts its predators.

VI. Macroevolution

Macroevolution deals with significant changes, for example; the development of upright posture.

SOURCE of Macroevolution: **Pre-adaptation** = the development of new features through the refinement of existing ones. The functions of the different types of forelimbs in different organisms are all different, but their anatomy (structure) is similar even though they are shaped differently. So changes have occurred in the **anatomical plan** rather than **redesigning** the forelimb for each organism.

Homologous Structures - In 1843, Richard Owen defined homology as "the same organ in different animals under every variety of form and function". Organs as different as a bat's wing, a seal's flipper, a cat's paw and a human hand have a common underlying structure of bones and muscles. Owen reasoned that there must be a common structural plan for all vertebrates, as well as for each class of vertebrates. Homologous traits that organisms posess are due to the fact that they shared a common ancestor. The appendages in the illustration have similar bone structure, but each appendage is used for a different purpose: grasping (human), running (cat), swimming (whale or seal), and flying (bat).

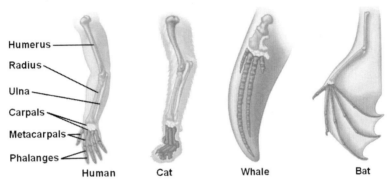

Humerus
Radius
Ulna
Carpals
Metacarpals
Phalanges

Human   Cat   Whale   Bat

VII. Evidence of Macroevolution

1. **Vestigial Organs** = genetically determined structures, once important to an ancestral species that with time, have lost most or all function in a given species, now are of no use in the current species (the evolved species still carries the DNA for the particular structure). So a structure that was once important, like the appendix, is of no use in humans. We only have a remnant of what used to be a large fermentation chamber.

2. **Embryological Development** = indicates common ancestry for many distantly related species. They may have similar embryos with similar structures like gill slits and tails.

3. **DNA** = by comparing DNA it is possible to see how similar the sequencing is between two closely related species. Cytochrome C is a protein found in all air-breathing organisms. The DNA that codes for it is similar in all primates (humans and apes). DNA comparisons are consistent with the fossil records.

VIII. Mass Extinction and Changes to the Environment

1. **Gradual**—Currently, **continental drift** (movement of the continents on the earth's crust) forces North America away from Europe (2 cm per year).

   Originally, there was one giant mass or super-continent called **Pangea** from which all the other continents formed (250 million years ago). Because of the changes to the environment, the organisms could not cope and this is believed to have caused the **Permean extinction**. In fact, it claimed over 90% of all organisms. For example, if a coastline was eliminated because two continents collided together, then the marine species along these coasts could no longer survive because now there is no water.

2. **Abrupt**—65 million years ago, dinosaurs became extinct due to an asteroid that hit the earth, which is believed to have caused the **Cretaceous extinction**. This claimed over 50% of all living organisms. The modern continents as we know them were shaped by this time.

The **Permian** and **Cretaceous** extinctions claimed much of the life that existed at those times. The following page illustrates the geological time line of our evolution. (see page 35)

Pesticide Resistance

Pesticides are not very effective for very long since some of the pests they were designed to kill have advantageous traits enabling them to survive the poison or its mechanism of action. These shrewd dudes then get married, make more pesty but zesty kids with anti-pesticide traits and continue to annoy us.

Artificial Selection

Artificial **Selection** (or selective breeding) is the intentional breeding for certain traits, or combination of traits. **Dog breeding** is a good example. Or **crop improvements**. Farmers select the best produce allowing only the plants (and animals) with desirable characteristics to reproduce, causing the evolution of farm stock. This process occurs because people (instead of nature) select which organisms get to reproduce.

Geological Time Scale

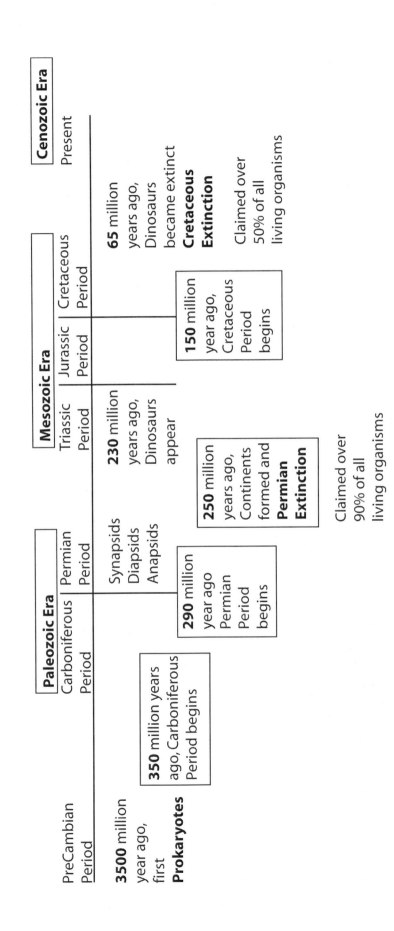

PreCambian Period

3500 million year ago, first **Prokaryotes**

350 million years ago, Carboniferous Period begins

Paleozoic Era

Carboniferous Period

Permian Period

Synapsids
Diapsids
Anapsids

290 million year ago Permian Period begins

250 million years ago, Continents formed and **Permian Extinction**

Claimed over 90% of all living organisms

Mesozoic Era

Triassic Period

230 million years ago, Dinosaurs appear

Jurassic Period

Cretaceous Period

150 million year ago, Cretaceous Period begins

65 million years ago, Dinosaurs became extinct **Cretaceous Extinction**

Claimed over 50% of all living organisms

Cenozoic Era

Present

Cell Membrane, Cell Transport and Membrane Attachments

7

Dividing Bacterial Cell – E. Coli

Unicellular Organism undergoing Binary Fission. Even though this is a bacterium, it has a cell wall like plants. Note that the DNA does not have a membrane to separate itself from the rest of the cellular contents.

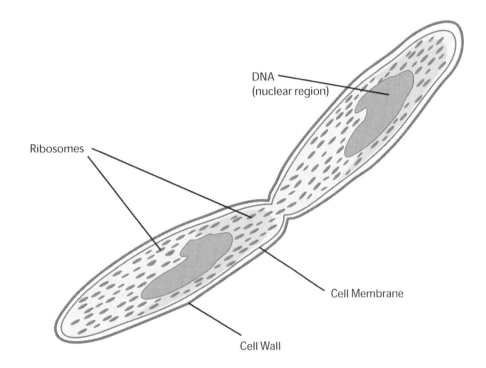

DNA
(nuclear region)

Ribosomes

Cell Membrane

Cell Wall

Basic Components of all Cells

Cells differ from one another by their size, shape and function. However, all cells have **three major components:**

1. Plasma Membrane (Cell Membrane)
In animals it's the **outermost** layer of the cell. In **plants** this membrane is further surrounded by a protective wall (the **cell wall**). In any event, this plasma membrane keeps the cell as a distinct entity because it's like a **boundary**. The membrane **selectively controls** what enters the cell and what exits. Therefore, the membrane does not keep the cell **isolated**; rather it allows

certain substances to continuously **move across** itself.

2. Cytoplasm (Cytosol or Protoplasm)

This is the **fluid inside of a cell** or the cellular fluid. It is also referred to as ICF or intra-cellular fluid. The cytoplasm has a **jello-like** consistency because it is a **semi-fluid**. The cytoplasm contains **water, salts, molecules, enzymes, filaments etc.** and little organs or sacs which are called **organelles**. Each organelle has a specific task. Most of these little organs are also surrounded by a **membrane** which is very similar to the plasma membrane in both structure and function. This is important to understand because it keeps each organelle separate from the other organelles. This enables each organelle to carry out its own metabolic reactions without any interference for another organelle.

3. DNA region (Deoxyribose Nucleic Acid)

This is an area found within the cell and it contains the **genetic material, DNA**. DNA carries the codes which determine an organism's traits like eye color or hair color. So, DNA contains the necessary information that eventually expresses an individual's traits. It does this by giving the instructions to make particular types of proteins. DNA is also passed on to the next generation and so forth. This is what we mean by **inheritance**. If both your mother and father have blue eyes there is a **high probability** that you will also inherit their blue eyes. If the genetic material is enclosed within a **membrane** (similar to the plasma membrane) like the other organelles, then it is called a **nucleus**. A cell with this type of arrangement has a proper nucleus. On the other hand, if this area is **not separated** from the rest of the cytoplasm by a membrane then this region is referred to as the **nuclear area** or the **nucleoid region** (for example, bacteria).

Animal Cell

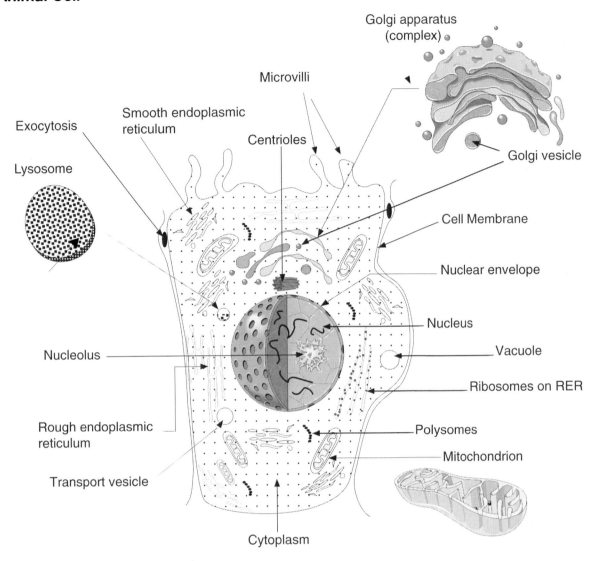

Golgi apparatus (complex)

Golgi vesicle

Microvilli

Smooth endoplasmic reticulum

Exocytosis

Centrioles

Lysosome

Cell Membrane

Nuclear envelope

Nucleus

Nucleolus

Vacuole

Ribosomes on RER

Rough endoplasmic reticulum

Polysomes

Transport vesicle

Mitochondrion

Cytoplasm

It is very important to realize that every cell has a **cell membrane** which we will discuss shortly. This membrane is made up of lipids and proteins. Actually there are two rows of them. Inside of the animal cell (and plant cells) are many small organs called organelles, for example, the nucleus, mithochondrion, endoplasmic reticulum, etc... These organelles also are contained within a **membrane**. The membrane that surrounds each organelle has the same structure (double row of lipids and proteins) as the cell membrane. The term "cell membrane" is reserved for the membrane which surrounds the entire cell. The term "membrane" is used to describe the structure which surrounds each organelle even though they all have the same characteristics like the cell membrane.

Model of Cell Membrane with Integral Proteins

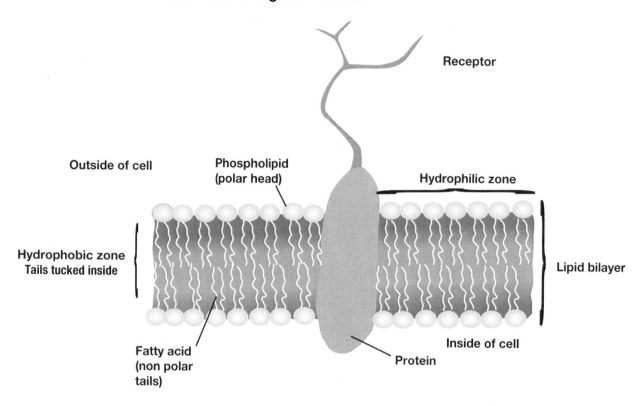

Cell Membranes

Membrane Structure and Function

Lipids

Several Types: TRG (triglycerides), Steroids, Sex hormones and:

Phospholipids - major component of membranes. They make up the cell membrane and the membranes of the organelles.

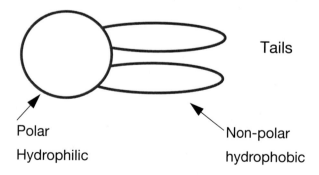

Structure of a Phospholipid

Fluid Mosaic Membrane Model

Since the phospholipids which make up the membrane have polar heads (hydrophilic) and non polar tails (hydrophobic), they assume a particular arrangement. The tails are tucked inside the structure so they are aligned far away from water. The heads like water and so are exposed to either the cytoplasm (inside the cell, ICF) or the extracelluar fluid (ECF) on the outside of the cell. These lipid molecules are not stationary. They are able to slide past one another and exchange places with their neighbors. This fluidity also permits the proteins which are embedded amongst the lipids to float around. Usually a protein extends from the outside of the cell, through the membrane and then into the interior of the cell.

This Model:

Explains the structure and function of membranes

It consists of a **bilipid layer**: double row of phospholipids

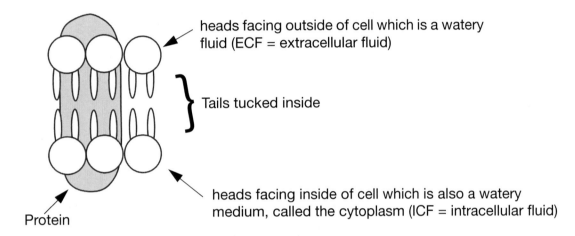

heads facing outside of cell which is a watery fluid (ECF = extracellular fluid)

Tails tucked inside

heads facing inside of cell which is also a watery medium, called the cytoplasm (ICF = intracellular fluid)

Protein

Fluidity—lipid molecules and the proteins move around

Functions of the cell membrane:

1) forms a closed compartment

2) separates the cell from its surroundings

3) provides structure

4) forms a barrier/covering

5) it has receptors on the proteins for the recognition of stimuli

6) the membrane responds to stimuli in an effort to regulate the metabolism of the cell

7) it provides an exchange between the cytoplasm and the outside of the cell

8) it maintains homeostasis—balances ionic concentrations and other substances, regulates temperature, etc.

_____
Last Name, First Name

General Biology
Dr. Abdirkin

Review Questions

6. Selection acts on individuals, but only populations evolve. Explain why this is true.

7. Distinguish between catastrophism and uniformitarianism.

8. Describe Lamark's theory of acquired inheritance.

9. What is the ultimate source of energy for all life?

10. In your own words, explain the two parts of photosynthesis.

11. What are the two principle types of molecules in the plasma membrane?

12. What are the principle functions of the plasma membrane?

13. What happens when a protein's receptor bonds to its specific signal molecule?

In the next section we will study how substances may enter and leave the cell:

Outline

I.   Passive Transport

II.   Active Transport

III. Transport of Large Particles

IV.   Membrane Attachments

Introduction

There are two main mechanisms cells use to bring substances in from the environment or remove wastes that need to be eliminated. One method does not require energy, called passive transport. The second mechanism, active transport. uses energy.

I. Passive Transport - small substances move in or out of the cell according to their concentration gradients directly across the cell membrane (diffusion and osmosis).

1. Diffusion

Diffusion is the movement of molecules from an area of **high concentration** to an area of **low concentration**. It occurs because molecules are in **constant random motion**. That is, they possess **kinetic energy** and this motion is referred to as **Brownian movement**.

Factors which affect the Diffusion Rate:

1. The larger the gradient, the faster will be the rate of diffusion.
2. The higher the temperature, the faster the molecules move, so diffusion will be more rapid.
3. The smaller the molecules, the faster they move. Therefore, small molecules diffuse easily and rapidly through the plasma membrane.

2. Osmosis—special type of diffusion that concerns water through a semi-permeable membrane. Water moves from a high water concentration to a low water concentration.

Rule of Thumb: water diffuses toward the side that has a greater concentration of solute particles

Illustration of Osmosis

Consider a **glass** tank divided by a **semi-permeable membrane**. On the **right side** there is a **glucose solution**. **Glucose** is the solute and the water is the solvent. When they are mixed together they make up a **glucose solution**. On the **left side** there is only **water**. The membrane is **not** permeable to glucose so **water diffuses to the right** (towards the side which is more concentrated in solute = definition of osmosis). This will increase the **volume** of solution on the right side. Obviously, the volume on the left side decreases. Actually, the glucose concentration on the right side is becoming more dilute because the volume of water increases on this side of the membrane. However, at a certain point **osmosis stops** because:

1. the two sides reach **equilibrium** (water molecules go back and forth across the membrane at the same rate; if one water molecule goes to the left, then one water

molecule on the left side goes to the right…at the same rate).

2. a **back pressure** (osmotic pressure) is created on the glucose side aimed towards the left side and it opposes any further water movement from the left side towards the right. **The size of this pressure depends on the solute concentration of glucose molecules and it is called the osmotic pressure.**

semi-permeable membrane

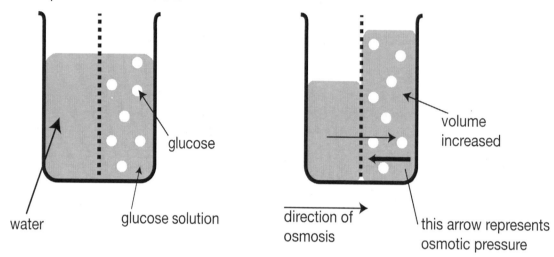

water   glucose solution

direction of osmosis

this arrow represents osmotic pressure

Physiological Solutions

Our **body fluids** have osmotic pressure which is related to the concentration of solute particles dissolved in them. Therefore, think of osmotic pressure as the solute concentration. When we go to replace body fluids for medical reasons, the fluids must have the identical osmotic pressure (concentration) as our fluids. The fluids used are called **Physiological Solutions** and there are two types:

1. 0.9 % **sodium chloride** solution (NaCl) - salt solution

2. 5.0 % **glucose** solution - sugar solution

Consider placing a **red blood cell** in various concentrations:

a) the red blood cell is placed in a **physiological solution** (for example, contact lens solution). This physiological solution is **isotonic** to the cell. This means the concentration in the red blood cell and the solution it is in are equal. "Iso" means the same. There is **no net movement** of water and the cell remains the **same size**. The cell remains the same size because both the internal and external solutions are of equal concentration.

b) now the red blood cell will be placed in a **hypotonic** solution (distilled water). This means that the concentration of the solution that the cell is placed in, is less than the concentration inside the red blood cell. So **water will diffuse into the cell** because it has a higher solute concentration and eventually the cell will expand and burst. This is called **hemolysis**.

c) the red blood cell is placed in a **hypertonic** solution (for example, a solution greater than a 5% glucose solution). In this case, the solution has a higher concentration so **water will move out of the red blood cell**. Remember, water diffuses towards the side that has the greater concentration. The cell shrivels up and shrinks. This process is called **crenation** (for example, consider a cucumber becoming a pickle).

RBC (Animal) Cells are placed in different solution concentrations to see the affect of osmosis:

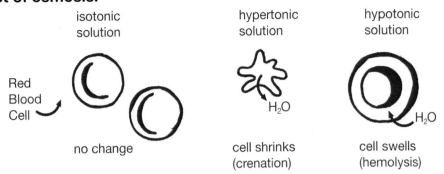

Passive Transport Proteins - This mechanism is also for small particles however, instead of ions or molecules passing directly through the membrane itself, they will diffuse through a membrane protein.

Passive Transport may involve two types of transport proteins. In both cases the transport occurs by diffusion, down the concentration gradient.

1. **Channel proteins:** this involves a protein that has a little **tunnel** extending from the outside of the cell to the inside. In other words, the channel extends the entire length of the protein (see figure). Substances may pass through this channel by **diffusion**. This is another way small molecules diffuse but this time with the help of a protein. The channel may have a **gate** which can open or close and this further regulates permeability. Sometimes there is **no gate** so the channel is always open.

2. **Carrier Proteins:** in this case, a specific protein actually combines with a specific substance and then transports it into or out of the cell depending on the concentration gradient. Here diffusion is going on with the help of this special protein and it enables the process to occur **more rapidly**. As such, this is called **facilitated diffusion**. The carrier proteins have receptors which are specific only for certain substances. The substance carried has to "fit" into the carrier's receptor in order to be transported.

Passive Transport through a Channel Protein

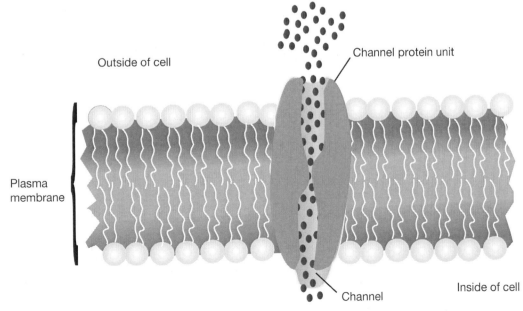

II. Active Transport - This is another mechanism to carry substances. However, it occurs without following the principles of diffusion.

1. moves substances **against** their concentration gradient or **uphill**.

2. requires energy in the form of adenosine triphosphate **(ATP)**.

3. continues until the solute becomes more concentrated on the side it is being pumped to. In other words, from an area of low concentration to one of high concentration (this is the **opposite of diffusion**)

4. **carrier proteins** are used to "pump" specific substances.

Mechanism of Action (active transport)

Analogy: think of a ski resort where the skiers are the substances and the chair lifts are the binding sites. At the bottom of the hill, the chair lift is tilted such that the skier can get right onto the lift so we say that the chair lift is **accessible**. The skier is then transported **uphill** to the top of the mountain and this requires the motor (**energy**) which operates the chair lift. At the top of the mountain the chair tilts such that the skier must get off (**inaccessible** binding site). Therefore, active transport requires energy to work the protein pump. In this case, the substance may be moved in any direction regardless of its concentration gradient. This is also specific for certain substances. The carrier protein has a receptor site which only allows certain substances to fit in and be transported ("lock and key" concept again like we saw in facilitated diffusion).

Types of Active Transport Pumps

1. **Calcium pump**: this pump transports **calcium** out of the cell.

2. **Acid pump**: this pump transports **acid** into the stomach. The acid is produced by the epithelial cells lining the stomach. The acid is HCl which can digest food.

3. **Drug-resistant pump**: this pump transports **chemotherapeutics** out of a cancer cell. Therefore, cancer cells may become resistant to certain drugs due to active transport via a carrier protein. The cancer cell is smart so it learns to get rid of what could destroy it.

4. **Sodium-potassium pump**: this is an **exchange transport pump** because it pumps **three sodiums out** of the cell while at the same time pumps **two potassiums into** the cell. This is one of the most important pumps in the body because it is necessary for many cellular activities such as **nerve conduction** and **muscle contraction**.

One third of all our energy is consumed in the operation of all the body's pumps.

All of the above transport mechanisms discussed thus far enable **small molecules** to cross the cell membrane either directly or with a transport protein, what about large molecules?

III. Transport of Large Particles

The **larger** particles **cannot** penetrate the plasma membrane via diffusion or be carried by transport proteins. However, if you recall, the membrane is **fluid** so by changing its **shape**, large molecules may be transported. The two processes involved are **endocytosis** and

exocytosis.

Endocytosis involves bringing substances into the cell. The membrane caves inwards and then balloons around the particle forming a vesicle. There are three types of **endocytosis: phagocytosis** (amoeba), **pinocyctosis** (cell drinking) and **receptor-mediated endocytosis**. Receptor mediated endocytosis involves specific molecules which bind to specific membrane receptors. These receptors are located in a shallow depression in the membrane called **coated pits**. When the specific substance binds to these receptors, the pit sinks into the cytoplasm forming a vesicle. As a result, the substance winds up inside the cell.

Exocytosis is involved with the **excretion** of wastes such as **sweat** and **urea**. It is also involved with the **secretion** of substances such as **hormones** and **saliva**. This is the exact opposite of endocytosis. There is a vesicle inside of the cell containing the substance the cell wants to get rid of. This vesicle fuses with the plasma membrane. The membrane opens up and the substance is released.

Endocytosis

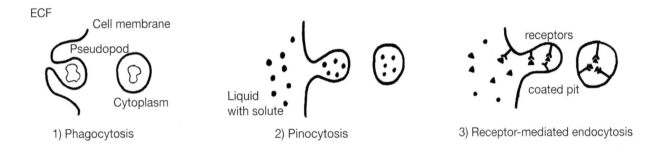

ECF
Cell membrane
Pseudopod
Cytoplasm

1) Phagocytosis

Liquid with solute

2) Pinocytosis

receptors
coated pit

3) Receptor-mediated endocytosis

IV. Membrane Attachments

There are several modifications in the cell membrane for attaching cells together and also for communication between cells (allowing inter-cellular communication):

Anchoring Junctions

1. **Tight junction**: this is an area where two cells are **sealed** together. Nothing may pass between them. It's as if they are **spot welded** in this area. Therefore, this junction seals off the inter-cellular space (space between two cells).

2. **Desmosomes**: this is an attachment which will **resist mechanical stress**. For example, this allows for the **elasticity** that skin possesses. In this case **protein fibers** extend from a region of each cell into the inter-cellular space. These fibers interact and **lock** together. Further support is provided by a **dense protein plaque** found just behind these fibers on the inside of a cell.

Communicating Junctions

Gap Junctions: these are areas where **small protein pipes** extend from one cell to the next. This allows **ions and small molecules** to pass directly and very quickly between cells. This is how cells "talk" to one another. Therefore, this junction facilitates communication via signals between cells. For example, these junctions are found between **cardiac muscle cells** so that electrical signals pass quickly to all the cardiac muscle cells simultaneously enabling the heart to subsequently contract in a coordinated fashion so that it acts as an efficient pump for circulating the blood.

Cell Junctions

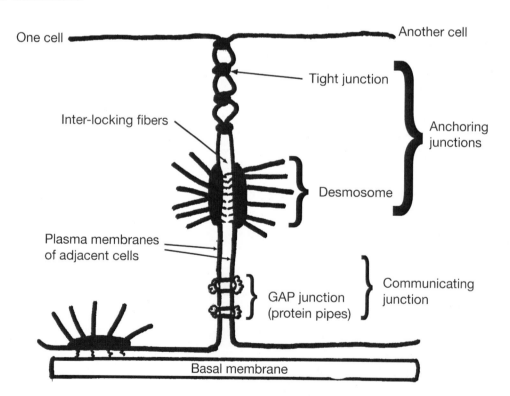

50

Cell Structures and their Functions

8

Bacterial Cell

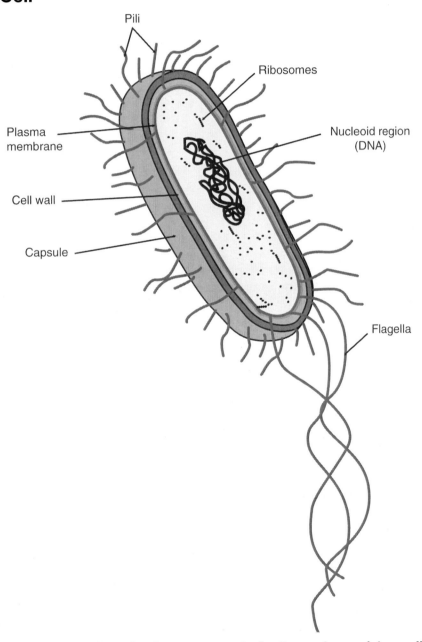

Pili

Ribosomes

Plasma membrane

Nucleoid region (DNA)

Cell wall

Capsule

Flagella

Remember, all cells have three basic components [cell membrane (also called the plasma membrane), DNA, and a cytoplasm]

Basic Cell Types: Prokaryotes and Eukaryotes:

Prokaryotes	*Eukaryotes*
unicellular	protists, multicellular organisms and animals
small	large
only have a plasma membrane	plasma membrane and more membranes around their organelles
circular DNA in one chromosome, located in the nuclear area = Nucleoid region	DNA in chromosomes, but in a proper membrane bound nucleus
lacks most organelles, but many ribosomes	many organelles with membranes: nucleus, ER, Golgi, lysosomes, ribosomes, vacuoles, mitochondria
also: cell wall, capsule, flagella, pili	

Prokaryotes

The word Prokaryote can be divided into "pro" which means before and "karyote" which means nucleus. So prokaryote means "before nucleus" therefore, these cells do not have a proper nucleus; instead they have a nuclear area or nucleoid. Some prokaryotes have a thick rigid cell wall which surrounds the plasma membrane. This is to help the cell maintain its shape and also for protection. In addition, some bacteria have a capsule around the cell wall. It is sticky so it can adhere to its host cell. For example, Streptococcus Mutans, is a common bacterium which glues itself onto your teeth using sugar, and then it causes tooth decay (see page 51 in APB).

Eukaryotes

The word Eukaryote can also be divided into "Eu" which means true, so a eukaryote has a true nucleus. This cell is much more sophisticated. It has many organelles with membranes. It is a larger cell and the DNA is inside of a membrane which is of course the nucleus. And the DNA is organized into several chromosomes.

Cell Organelles (Eukaryotes)

1. Mitochondrion

This organelle is found in both plants and animals, and produces **ATP**. ATP has three phosphate groups attached to it. When ATP is utilized, an enzyme called **ATPase** breaks the bond between the **second and third** phosphate group. Therefore, the third phosphate group is set free. By breaking this bond, a great deal of **usable energy** is released to power cellular reactions. In fact, the energy provided by ATP is used for **growth, movement, and repair**. What about the left over part of the ATP molecule which has lost a phosphate group? It becomes **ADP** or adenosine diphosphate. ADP will undergo another reaction whereby it picks up a **phosphate group,** forms **ATP** again so that it is **recycled** and may be reused. In this way, the ATP supply is constantly renewed. ATP is transferred around the cell to various locations where it is needed. The mitchondrion has a double membrane. The outer one is smooth yet the inner one is highly folded to increase the surface area to carry out the production of ATP and other important reactions. The mitochondrion has its own DNA even though it is no longer an independent cell.

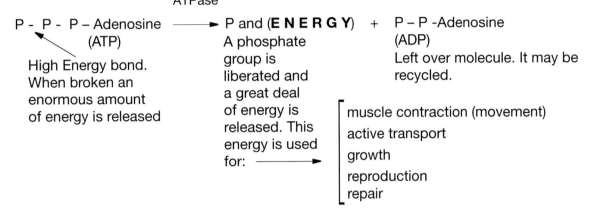

2. **Nucleus:** chromosomes (DNA inside)

    DNA→ RNA→ cytoplasm, here RNA is read by a ribosome complex so amino acids are brought in and linked together to form proteins. When DNA is all coiled up and wrapped around itself it forms the structure we call a **chromosome**. When DNA unwinds, uncoils and untangles itself, it is a very long molecule. In this case it is called a **chromatin**. DNA needs to unwind like this so it can be copied to make more of itself during replication (duplication) or to serve as a template to make RNA (transcription).

3. **Nucleoli:** dense area in nucleus
    makes ribosomal parts

4. **Nuclear Envelope**—double layered membrane

    1. nuclear pores—for RNA to get out and holds double membrane together, is selective

    2. outer membrane continues into ER system

5. **Ribosomes**—site of protein synthesis. They may be:

    1. attached to ER forming a rough endoplasmic reticulum (RER)

    2. attached to each other—polysome

    3. free in the cytoplasm

    Note: Proteins are assembled on the surface of the RER. The ribosomes there read messenger RNA; amino acids are linked together and eventually a protein is formed. Now the protein enters inside of the RER because much more needs to be done to it before it is fully functional.

6. **Endoplasmic Reticulum**

tunnels and sacs

lumen

types:

1) RER—ribosomes attached to ER

   a) elaborateses **proteins** once they are threaded inside of their lumen. These proteins were assembled on the surface of the ER at the ribosome.

   b) makes new **membrane material** for its own membrane or other membranes (repair)

2) SER—no ribosomes. It is found in cells involved with:

   a) **lipid metabolism**, like the formation of cholesterol and steroid hormones in the liver

   b) **detoxification** of chemicals. This would occur in liver cells also which are part of the drug metabolizing system (DMS).

   c) storage of Calcium ions for **muscle contraction**. The calcium is necessary and released so muscle cells can contract.

7. **Golgi Apparatus**:

flat membranous sacs

vesicles from ER fuse to it, which gets proteins (inside vesicle) to the inside of Golgi. Golgi then modifies, sorts and packages the proteins even further. This process repeats as the proteins travels through all the sacs. Eventually, a final vesicle emerges called the *transport vesicle*, which can go off to:

a) become a **lysosome** which contains hydrolytic enzymes, **or the vesicle goes to**

b) the plasma membrane where by **exocytosis** gets its contents (proteins) discharged from this cell to the extracellular fluid.

8. **Lysosomes**:

• membrane bound sacs

• contain digestive enzymes (hydrolytic enzymes)

• fuse with other vesicles that contain materials which cell wants to get rid of, for example:

       digested food remains

       damaged cellular debris

       viruses and bacteria

After the lysosome is done, any of these things (food, debris, foreign organisms) are broken down to their basic building blocks, which are reused to make new molecules. Therefore, lysosomes are recycling centers.

Endomembrane System

From the outer nuclear membrane to the ER, through the golgi apparatus, to the plasma membrane - all of this is considered the **endomembrane system.**

The **vesicle** which is produced by the endoplasmic reticulum (which contains a protein) either goes off to the **Gogli Appartus** or its contents may become **integrated and inserted** into **membranes** like the cell membrane or even the membranes of the other organelles or even into the ER membrane. Therefore, new membrane material is added to **repair or replace** existing membranes.

The **final vesicle** which emerges from the Golgi Apparatus contains elaborated and functional proteins:

1. In the cells of the **digestive system**, the Golgi Apparatus would manufacture **digestive enzymes** (proteins) and **mucus** (protein).

2. The Golgi Appartus in the cells of an endocrine gland **(endocrine system)** would produce **hormones** (also proteins). Estrogen and testosterone are examples of steroid hormones produced in the testes and ovaries, respectively. The gonads are part of the endocrine system. An anabolic steroid is a synthetic form of testosterone.

   The vesicles (which contain the proteins) go to the plasma membrane and discharge their contents by **exocytosis.** In this way, important proteins are exported to other cells, the extracellular fluid (ECF), the blood, or into lumens.

3. If the final vesicle, which emerges from the Golgi, contains **hydrolytic enzymes** (proteins), it may become a **lysosome** which can "attack" foreign viruses and bacteria by fusing with them and then "eating" them up using the enzymes it posses. They even engulf **damaged** or worn out organelles. In any event, lysosomes break down **macromolecules** to their basic constituents, so the result of all lysosomal digestion is always **amino acids, fatty acids** and **sugars**. These substances may then be reassembled by the same cell the lysosome is in, or another cell. Cells reconstruct the proteins, lipids and carbohydrates that they need from these basic units (amino acids, fatty acids and sugars). So the lysosome is a **recycling center.**

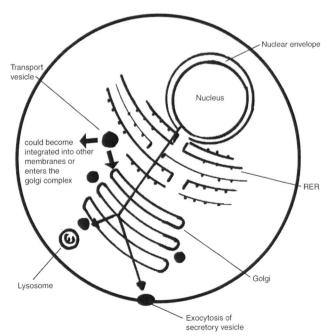

55

Cytoskeleton (Eukaryote Cells)

- The cytoskeleton is a network of filaments
  1. reinforces plasma membrane
  2. carries out movement: "cytoplasmic streaming"
  3. may be disassembled, moved and reassembled (like a scaflod)
  4. provides framework—cell shape

- There are 3 types of fibers (proteins) which make up the cytoskeleton
  1. microtubules—largest
  2. microfilaments—smallest
  3. intermediate filaments—intermediate

1. Microtubules

Theses are the thickest filaments and are actually hollow tubes made up of thousands of **protein subunits.**

These filaments may be organized to form **cilia and flagella** both of which are cytoplasmic extensions. Both function by a "beating whip-like action. Flagella propel cells like sperm and bacteria. Cilia are shorter, hair-like and more numerous, and they move debris and mucus past the cells from which they extend. For example, you would find cilia in the cells of the respiratory passages in order to slide any foreign material (mixed with mucous) towards the opening of the mouth thereby preventing it from entering the trachea and lungs. Then the mucus is expectorated.

Microtubules are also involved in **cell division**. This is when a cell duplicates itself and makes two daughter cells from the original. Each daughter cell is identical to the original.

Microtubules make up a structure called a **centriole**. The centrioles are involved in organizing the mitotic spindle in animal cells. This spindle is necessary for cell division. Plant cells also have to create a spindle apparatus during division however, centrioles are not involved. Plants do not contain centrioles.

2. Microfilaments

These are the thinnest filaments and are made up of protein molecules called actin. Microfilaments give strength and stiffen the **microvilli** found in intestinal cells. The microvilli make up the **brush border** which increases the surface area for absorption.

Microfilaments also account for **ameboide movement** which is the pushing and pulling of the amoebae's cell membrane to change its shape enabling it to move along.

However, the main function of the microfilaments is **"cytoplasmic streaming"** or intracellular movement. There is constant circular movement in the cytoplasm and these fibers provide tracks for the organelles and vesicles to slide on and go around the cell to change locations.

Microfilaments are also part of the **contractile mechanism** in muscle cells.

Plant Cells

Plant cells have three features that animal cells do not have and they are plastids, cell walls and large vacuoles:

1. Plastids

Plastids are organelles found only in plants. There are three types:

   a) **Chloroplasts** are green plastids which contain chlorophyll, the pigment which traps the sunlight to carry out the reactions involved in photosynthesis.

   b) **Chromoplasts** are plastids which make yellow and orange pigments for the roots, fruits and flowers.

   c) **Amyloplasts** are plastids that store starch and so would be abundant in potatoes.

2. Cell Wall

The cell wall is thick, located outside the plasma membrane and is made up of **cellulose** which maintains the cell's shape, provides support, and gives structure to the cell but is **flexible**. For example, cellulose enables the stem of a plant to be sturdy and hold up the leaves and flowers yet the stem is flexible enough to withstand the wind without snapping.

The cell wall has **pores** (small openings). The pores allow **water** to enter the plant cell which establishes an **outward pressure** once inside. This pressure expands the plant cell with its plasma membrane outwards so that it fills out the entire space provided by the cell wall. In other words, due to the **water pressure**, the plasma membrane gets pushed out and up against the cell wall. Therefore, the plant **cell fills out the space defined by the cell wall.** This outward pressure is also called **turgor pressure**.

These pores also allow **for intercellular communication.**

In addition, the cell walls of adjacent plant cells are **cemented** together.

3. Vacuoles

These are large sacs of fluid enclosed within a membrane. Usually a plant cell has one for storage purposes and it is centrally located. Due to their size, most of the plant's cell volume is occupied by one of these vacuoles and, as such the vacuole pushes all the other organelles to the periphery of the cell. These vacuoles may hold food, pigments or in some cases hold toxins that the plant produces. The **toxins** must be contained in a vacuole otherwise they would be free to destroy the cell itself (by poisoning itself or suicide). What is the purpose of having the toxins? If an animal comes along and starts to eat a plant that contains toxins, the poison will be released and the animal will either get very sick or die. The animal eventually learns to stay away from these types of plants. Therefore, the toxins serve to protect the plant from its **predators**.

Animal cells also have vacuoles for storage however, they are called vesicles. The secretory or transport vesicles produced in the endomembrane processing system can be referred to as vacuoles. The vesicles in endo and exocytosis are also sometimes referred to as vacuoles.

_____
Last Name, First Name

Review Questions

14. Explain osmosis.

15. What would be the fate of an animal cell immersed in a hypertonic solution?

16. Describe active transport.

17. Describe eukaryotic cells.

18. When comparing plant and animal cells, which organelles are unique to plants?

19. What is the difference between chromatin and chromosomes?

20. Where are ribosomes found in a cell?

21. What is the function of lysosomes?

Histology: The Tissues

Types of Tissues

Outline: There are four types of tissues yet, there are many subdivisions.

I. Epithelial Tissue

simple or stratified

squamous, cubiodal or coulmnar

II. Connective Tissue

1. Embryonic

2. Connective tissue proper: Reticular

                                                      Loose

                                                      Adipose

                                                      Dense

                                                      Elastic

3. Cartilage: Hyaline, Elastic, Fibrocartilage

4. Bone: Spongy and Compact

5. Vascular (Blood):   Formed elements and Plasma

III. Muscle Tissue: Smooth, Cardiac, Skeletal

IV. Nerve Tissue: Neurons, Neuroglia

Epithelial Tissue

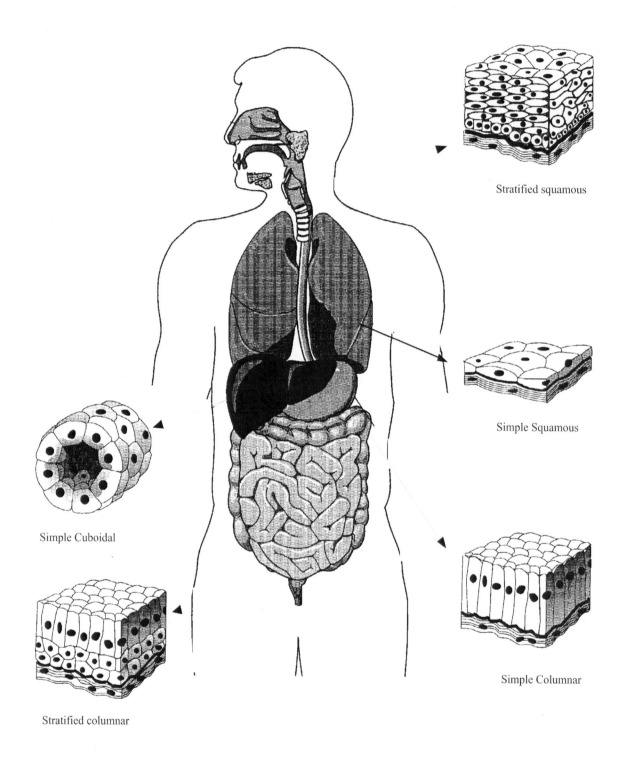

Stratified squamous

Simple Squamous

Simple Cuboidal

Simple Columnar

Stratified columnar

Common types of epithelial tissues and where they may be found.

Connective Tissue

Ground Substance

Reticular fibers

Fibroblast

Collagen fibers

Elastic fibers

Histology is the study of tissues, which then provides us with an understanding of an **organ's physiology** (how it functions) as well as its **structure** (what it looks like - it's architecture). By knowing the structure of normal tissues, a **pathologist** would be able to recognize and identify any **abnormalities** like those found in diseased tissues. From these studies a **diagnosis** could be made.

There are four main types of tissues. Learn the outline on page 61 of APB in order to keep track of the various tissues and their subtypes.

1. Epithelial tissue

Epithelium is found on every body surface like the skin and it lines every body cavity. It covers and lines:

1. **interior surfaces** (lumens: inside mouth, nasal cavity, digestive tract, inside blood vessels and also reproductive tubes and tracts). Sometimes epithelial tissue is given a more specific name depending on its location. For example, when it lines the interior of blood vessels, it is more accurate to refer to it as endothelium.....just a slight name change. It also lines the respiratory passages and in this area is called respiratory epithelium. Here it secretes mucus, which is involved with trapping any dust particles one may inhale. Since these epithelial cells also have cilia, the dust-entrapped mucus is swept towards the throat to be expectorated. Epithelial tissue also lines small ducts like those of the salivary glands.

2. **exterior surface** linings (skin and outer layer of organs)

Epithelial cells are closely packed (attached by junctions) so they form a continuous layer/ sheet.

Epithelial cells exist in three different shapes:

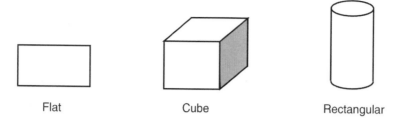

Flat   Cube   Rectangular

Flat epithelial cells are called **squamous** epithelium.

Cube shaped epithelial cells are called **cuboidal** epithelium.

Rectangular epithelial cells are called **columnar** epithelium.

When there is only a **single layer** of epithelial cells, the tissue is classified according to the shape of the cells. For example, if there are several cuboidal epithelial cells but all in a **single layer** then it is called **simple cuboidal epithelium**. If there are **two to several layers** of cells, the tissue is classified by the shape of the cells found on the **upper-most layer**. Therefore, if there are 9 layers of cuboidal cells covered by a top layer of squamous cells then this tissue is **stratified squamous epithelium**. The bottom layer of cells in all the various types of epithelial tissues rests on what is called the **basement membrane** which is another type of tissue called connective tissue. This layer is not to be confused with epithelial cells.

2. Connective tissue

This type of tissue is found **throughout** the body; in fact it's the most abundant tissue. With the exception of cartilage connective tissue, all the other types are **well vascularized**. This means that the tissue is supplied by **many blood vessels** to provide nutrients. Since connective tissue may replicate, it is involved with organ repair. It also contains cells that are involved with immunity. All connective tissues are composed of cells which make fibers and matrix. These cells are called fibroblasts.

Types: A) embryonic (mesenchyme and Wharton's Jelly)

                  B) connective tissue proper: loose, dense, elastic, reticular, and adipose

                  C) cartilage: hyaline, fibrocartilage, elastic

                  D) bone

                  E) vascular

Types of Connective Tissue

A. Embryonic Connective Tissue

Suffice is to say that this tissue is a jelly-like material found inside of the umbilical cord. It may be seen when the cord is cut and is also called **Wharton's Jelly**.

B. Connective Tissue Proper

Generalities (which also apply to all of the other connective tissues):

1. The **CELLS** in connective tissue are called **fibroblasts** which are star-shaped (see page 8 of APB).

2. These cells make the **FIBERS** of which there are three types:

   a) **Collagen fibers** are made of collagen. Collagen fibers consist of three alpha helixes braided together like a rope. This is what accounts for its strength.

   b) **Elastic fibers** are long and threadlike. They may stretch up to one and a half times their original length. They also recoil and are made of a substance called elastin

   c) **Reticular fibers** are thin fibers that form a network or web called a stroma.

3. The fibroblasts as we already mentioned make the **MATRIX** which is the medium in which the fibroblasts and fibers are located. Matrix is also called **intercellular material** or **ground substance** or even **ECF** (extracellular fluid). Its consistency varies from watery to gel-like to very dense and hard. The classification of connective tissue is based on the **type of matrix present**.

4. In addition to the fibroblasts, **OTHER CELLS** may or may not be present. Some of the other cells which appear are:

   Macrophages: clean up debris

   Mast Cells: produce heparin (anticoagulant) and histamine (vasodilator)

   Plasma Cells: produce antibodies against foreign antigens like bacteria

   Leukocytes: involved in the inflammatory process

5. **TYPES of connective tissue proper**:

   Reticular—framework of organs. (i.e. spleen)

   Loose—under skin—flexibility, connects skin to muscle

   Adipose—insulates, padding, food reservoir

   Dense—bone to muscle (i.e. tendons)

   Elastic—large arteries, vocal chords, bronchi

C. Cartilage

cells: chondrocytes (fibroblasts)

flexible, elastic, **No** blood supply

Types: **Hyaline**—"gristle" (i.e. nose, trachea, ribs to sternum)

   Elastic—dense network (i.e. external ear)

   Fibrocartilage—durable shock absorber (i.e. intervertebral discs)

D. Bone

cells: osteoblasts and osteocytes

most rigid, highly vascularized

serves as a calcium storage

Types: **spongy**—porous, light
                      red bone marrow
              compact—hard, dense
                      yellow bone marrow

E. Vascular (Blood)
   Plasma = matrix

   Formed elements: RBC (erythrocytes)
                    WBC (leukocytes)
                    platelets (thrombocytes)

3. Muscle Tissue

elongated muscles cells: called muscle fibers due to their length

provides movement and locomotion

there is a contractile mechanism in muscle cells which causes their shortening

types: 1—smooth
          2—cardiac
          3—skeletal

1. **Smooth muscle tissue:** the cells are **elongated** so they are also referred to as **smooth muscle fibers**. The cell shape is called **fusiform** or **spindle shape** because the cell tapers off at each end (see page 8). There are **no bands** or striations in these cells. This muscle would be found in the **walls of the gastrointestinal tract** to mix and propel the food forward. It would be found in the **arteries** to propel the blood and also in the **organs** (viscera). Smooth muscle is under **involuntary** control. It is also found in the urinary passages and reproductive tubes/ducts. The contractions produced by these muscles is slow but sustained.

2. **Cardiac muscle tissue:** the cells here are also long but they branch or we say they bifurcate. They are **striated**, under **rhythmic involuntary** or **automatic control** and make up the **walls of the heart**. The cardiac muscle cells are held together at regions called **intercalated discs**. These regions not only have **desmosomes** to anchor one cardiac muscle cell to the next but they also have **gap junctions** so that the electrical signals may be transmitted to all the cells simultaneously. Thanks to these modifications of the cell's membranes, the electrical signal is transmitted to all the heart cells (gap junctions) simultaneously enabling them to contract in unison (since they are anchored to one another: desmosomes), which causes the heart to work like a pump that propels the blood efficiently.

3. **Skeletal muscle tissue:** the cells (or fibers) are long and cylindrical and they have **striations**. Skeletal muscle is attached to bone for **voluntary** movement. Some examples of skeletal muscles are the biceps and triceps.

4. Nervous Tissue

1. The **neurons** can respond to physical and chemical **stimuli**, they **conduct impulses**, they **store memory and think**. They are the most **specialized** cells in the body and one of their principle roles is to **regulate the activity of other organs**.

2. **Neuroglia**--These are the cells which support, nourish and protect the neurons. There are several types each, one has a specific function.

The Neuron

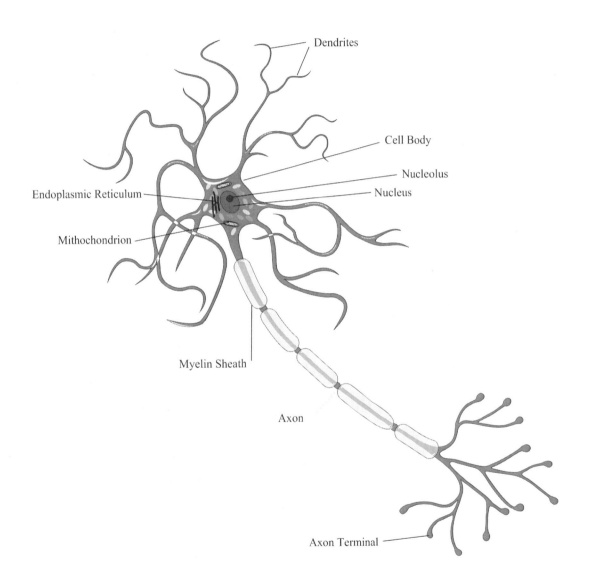

Entomology: Arthropods 10

Insects

Largest number of animals
Most successful of the animals
Endless variety of creatures
Habitats: land, water and air

The Insect Body

internal and external anatomy

1. Common features: What is an insect
Body:
1. head
2. chest (thorax): 4 wings (2 pairs or could be only 1 pair)
3. abdomen

2. Locomotion
Legs:
Spade-like—to dig
Plier-like—to grip
Roll balls
Stiff
Jumping and leaping
Paddle-like (fins and flippers)

Wings:
Hard outer covers
Folding back
Decorated
Translucent
Vibrate

3. Senses
a) Eyes—compound
b) Antennae
c) Voice—thorax (buzzing and chirping)
d) Hearing—abdomen

4. Eating
Mouths: chewing
straw—piercing, sucking
long tube-like—siphoning
sponging
jaws

5. Reproduction
Eggs
Abdomen
Valves
Saw-like egg laying organ

The Rhythm of Life

life cycle, adaptation methods to seasons, pupal development

1. Preparing the body for winter
Disappearance of food
Longer nights, lower temperature
Cannot store food, nor migrate
Instinct to survive
Drain water
Pack fat
Spiracles

2. Finding a place to winter
Underground
Tree trunks
Build quilt
Cocoon

3. New life
Metamorphosis
Eggs → larva → pupa → adult
Chrysalis
Mantis egg case
Egg-laying organ
Carpet of hairs

4. Winter
Hibernation
Carpet of leaves
Cracks of rock
Caves

5. Early risers
Warmth (temperature) is the signal
Lose protection

6. Spring awakening
Rains
Plant food
Cocoon
Chrysalis

7. The hunt
Territory
Plant eating
Hunting insects (mantis, wasps)—balance between animals and plants

Survival Tactics

methods of defense, long term success

1. Fighting off enemies
Methods of self defense
Sting
Smell
Shaking and swinging

2. Camouflage
Holding still
Insects can look like leaves or branches or thorns
There are three methods:
    a) protective resemblance - blend into environment
    b) protective coloration - blend into colors around them
    c) warning coloration - for defense

3. Escaping predators
Pockets
Leaf-rolling caterpillar
Playing dead (automatic reaction)

4. Natural selection
Changing colors
Inchworm moths
Fitting to the surrounds
Imitation
Instinct for self defense
Loss of camouflage
Hunt/hunted
Attackers/prey

Define:

Abdomen

Antennae

Camouflage

Caterpillar

Chrysalis

Cocoon

Compound Eye

Grub

Hibernation

Instinct

Larva

Lens (eye)

Metamorphosis

Natural selection

Nectar

Parasitic

Protective coloration

Protective resemblance

Pupa

Silk

Spiracle

Warning coloration

Plant Diversity

11

Classification of Land Plants

Classification	Common Name	Comments	Illustration
1. Nonvascular Plants (Seedless Plants) Division Bryophtya Division Hepatophyta Division Anthocerophyta	Mosses Liverworts Hornworts		
2. Vascular Plants (Seedless Plants) Division Lycophyta Division Sphenophyta Division Pterophyta	 Club Mosses Horsetails Ferns	From 300 million years ago Spore bearing	
3. Seed Plants *a) Gymnosperms* Division Coniferophyta Division Cycadophyta→ → Division Ginkgophyta Division Gnetophyta *b) Angiosperms* Division Anthophyta	 Conifers Sago Palms Cycads→ Ginkgo Gnetae Flowering plants	 **Cycads:** Palm-like leaves with short woody stems (since prehistoric times)	

Evolution of Plants

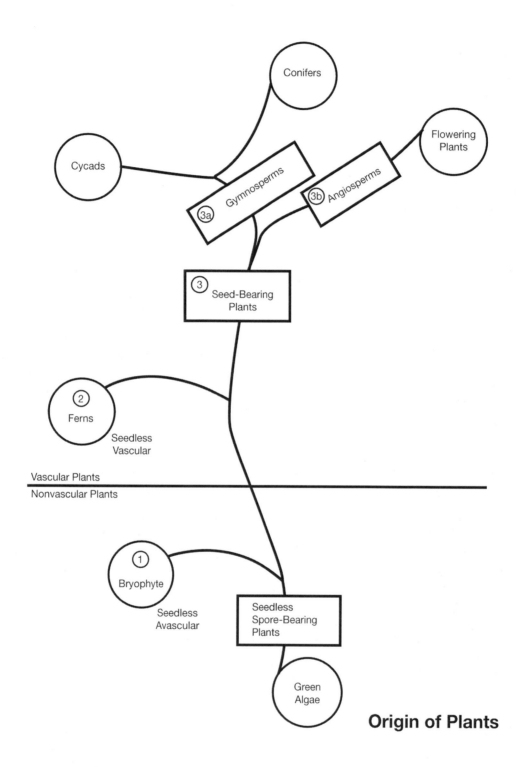

Conifers

Flowering Plants

Cycads

3a Gymnosperms

3b Angiosperms

3 Seed-Bearing Plants

2 Ferns

Seedless Vascular

Vascular Plants

Nonvascular Plants

1 Bryophyte

Seedless Avascular

Seedless Spore-Bearing Plants

Green Algae

Origin of Plants

Plants

In the history of life on earth, **first the plants colonized the land**, and then came the animals. The arrival of plants on land was a major event. Evidence suggests that the first land plants were related to **green algae** which lived in the water. These primitive plants had to survive the conditions present on land, such as **temperature variations** and **gravitational forces**. So new and different adaptations had to evolve for plants to survive on land. For example, on land, plants are no longer bathed in water and so they had to develop:

1. **vascular tissues** to move materials and water throughout their bodies.

2. **waxy cuticle** which covers their body and prevents it from drying out in the sun.

The plants transformed the landscape and made it possible for **prokaryotes** to exist as well as **herbivorous animals** and their **predators**.

Classification of plants:

Land plants can be classified as (see page 75 of APB):

1. **Nonvascular and seedless**: here we have the **bryophytes** which are the mosses

2. **Vascular and seedless**: include, the **ferns** which appeared 300 million years ago and are **spore** bearing

3. **Seed Plants**:

   a) **Gymnosperms**: which include the **conifers** or cone bearing plants and also the **cycads** which have palm-like leaves with short woody stems (these have been around since prehistoric times.

   b) **Angiosperms**: these are the **flowering** plants

Haploid / Diploid Generations

Before we can understand the plant life cycle, we need to learn something about chromosomes and we shall use **humans** to illustrate the point. Except for the sex cells in humans, all the other cells in the body each have **46 chromosomes**. The **sex cells** are also called the **gametes**: in the male, the gametes are the **sperm** and in the female they are the **ovum**. These cells only have half the number of chromosomes or **23**. This is called the **haploid number**. When **fertilization** occurs, each parent contributes 23 chromosomes to the offspring which reestablishes the **diploid number** of chromosomes (which in humans is 46). Therefore, if n = the **haploid** number, then 2n is the **diploid** number. In humans **n = 23**. Plants also have sex cells therefore, they have haploid sex cells which originate from a diploid plant. However, the plant life cycle alternates between gametophytes and sporophytes.

Plant life cycle:

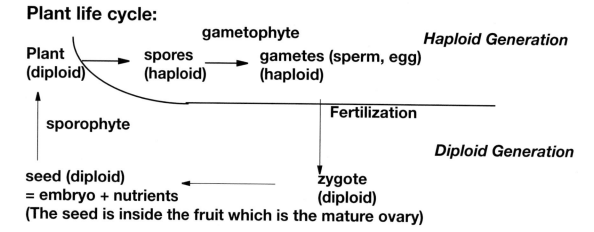

The plant life cycle alternates between the haploid and diploid generations:

The multicellular sporophyte is diploid and it produces spores by meiosis. The spores which are haploid grow into a gametophyte by mitosis. Therefore, haploid spores grow into a multicellular individual. This is a conspicuous stage in mosses and ferns. Next, the gametophyte produces gametes by mitosis. The gametes fuse to produce a new diploid sporophyte.

On the other hand, a mature **animal** (diploid) produces haploid gametes directly by meiosis. There are no spores.

Some plants may reproduce asexually from a vegetative piece of the original plant (stem or root). There are natural **vegetative structures** like rhizomes and stolons which some plants produce. Scientists can **cut and graft** plants to select for certain traits. This is also achieved through asexual reproduction.

Plant Anatomy

12

Gymnosperms and Angiosperms

I. Gymnosperms

Conifers (pine tree)
    Since Carboniferous Period
    Cone-bearing
    Widespread
    Northern lands
    Dry, cool climates
    Short growing season
    Adapted to harsh winter
    Branches bend
    Needle-like leaves: resist drying out and remain on tree throughout year
    Supply lumber and paper

II. Angiosperms

Flowering
    All land areas
    80% of all plants
    Food and fiber
    Include:
        1. grains   3. vegetation   5. flax
        2. fruit trees   4. cotton   6. fine hardwoods

Anatomy of Flower

Leaves
Cells
Flower
Stem - is situated below the pedicel
Sepals
Petals
Pedicel - is the stalk that supports the flower
Receptacle
Corolla - is the term used to describe the shape of all the petals collectively
Reproductive structures:
    Male = **Stamen:**   Female = **Carpel or Pistil:**
        Anther   Stigma
        Filament   Style
                          Ovary

Flower Anatomy

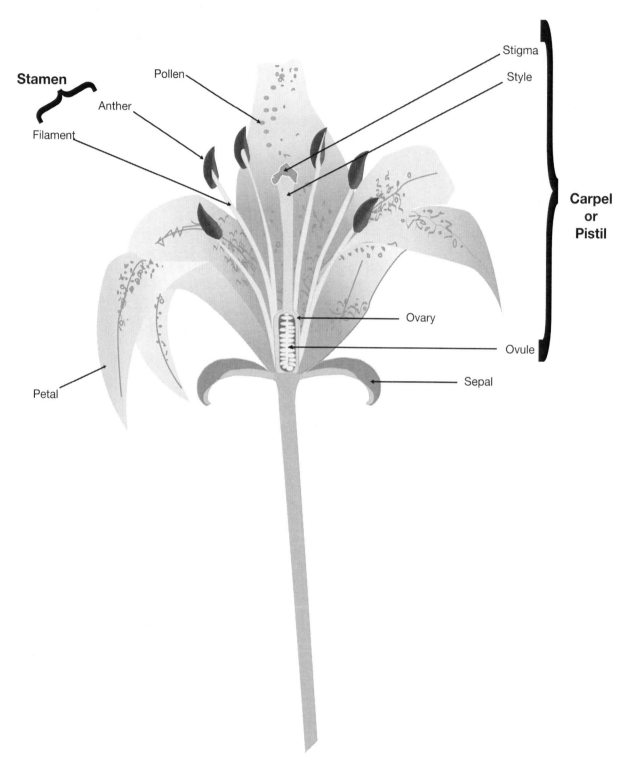

The pollen has been released from the anther. It travels over to the sticky receptive tip called the stigma (of the same plant). This illustrates **self-pollination**.

Angiosperm Life Cycle

The **anther** produces the **pollen grains** which manage to land on the **stigma**. The pollen grain now grows a tube (**pollen tube**) down through the style eventually reaching an **egg**. Next the sperm go through this tube to get to the egg. The eggs are located inside one of the many **ovules**. Fertilization occurs, a **zygote** forms, and an **embryo** results which has a food supply and is contained in a seed. **Endosperm** is the tissue produced in a seed to nourish the embryo. Usually it is starch but can contain proteins and oils. The **cotyledon** or seed leaf of the embryo is inside the seed and is usually the first leaf to germinate. The seed was derived from the ovule compartment. At the same time, the ovary wall thickens and forms the **fruit**. Therefore, a fruit forms containing the **seeds**. An animal may eat this fruit. The seeds will not be digested so they leave the animal when it defecates. Under the proper conditions, the seed germinates and grows into a plant which will have both the male and female reproductive structures inside of its flowers. Gametes will be produced to start the process all over again.

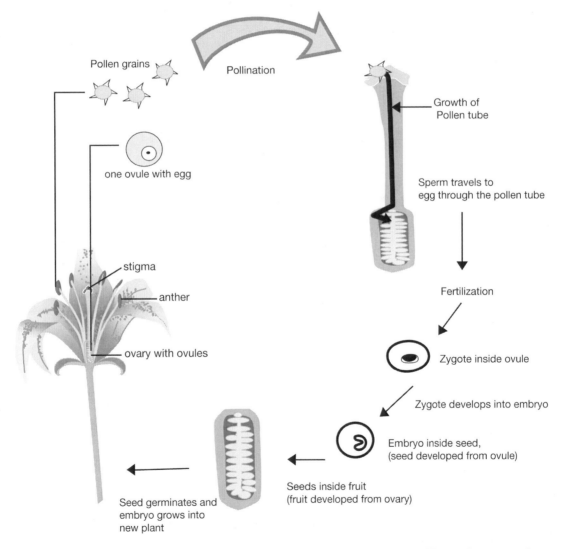

Fertilization in angiosperms occurs 12 hours after pollination. Therefore, a plant may produce seeds in just a few days or weeks. Plants then, reproduce very rapidly.

Comparison of the Adaptations of Gymnosperms and Angiosperms

Gymnosperms only	Both Gymnosperms and Angiosperms	Angiosperms only
No flowers or fruit	Pollen grain	Ovary
	Internal fertilization	Fruit
	Ovule	Flowers
	Seed	Annuals and perennials
	Vascular tissue	

Flower Morphology

Features of Flowers:

Number of petals

Number of sepals

Color

Scent (+/-)

Nectar (+/-)

Shape

Landing platform (+/-)

Pollinators

Key to Pollination

	Pollinator	Features of Petals	Flower Shape	Scent
1.	**Wind**	reduced petals		no odor
2.	**a) Moth**	white petals		sweet odor
	b) Bat	white petals		fruit-like odor
	c) Fly	white petals		odor of sweat or feces
3.	**a) Bee**	colored petals; blue, yellow or orange	irregular shape, landing platform	
	b) Beetle	colored petals	regular	fruity, spicy or sweet odor
4.	**a) Butterfly**	colored petals	tubular	strong sweet odor
	b) Humming bird	colored petals: red	tubalar	little or no odor

Seed Dispersal and Classification of Fruit

13

Fruit Lab

Strawberry

Walnut

Sunflower

Okra

Green beans

Peach

Green squash (zucchini)

Green pepper

Tomato

Apple

Pear

Rice

Pineapple

Avocado

Orange

Pistachio nuts

Coconut

Egg plant

Pea pod

Mango

Cherries

Plum

Lemon

Fruits grown in Dade County

Avocado

Banana

Cherry

Carambola

Guava

Key lime

Kumquat

Mango

Papaya

Passion fruit

Apple

Classification of Fruits

A. Simple Fruits

These fruits develop from a single ovary

They may be classified as **dry** and **fleshy** fruits (see page 87)

B. Compound Fruits

These are fruits which have **multiple ovaries** and there are two types:

1. **Multiple fruits**: consider a group of separate flowers and they are tightly clustered together. The **ovary walls** of each flower **fuse together** and become incorporated into one fruit. Therefore, multiple fruits are formed from the **ovaries of many flowers**. An example of a multiple fruit is the pineapple.

2. **Aggregate fruits**: in this case we have a **single flower** with **several separate carpals.** As such there are **several ovaries** which form the fruit. Therefore, aggregate fruits are formed from the **ovaries of one flower**. For example, a strawberry or blackberry.

Key to Fruits

Simple Fruits

I. Dry fruits (at maturity)

  A. Fruits with **one seed**

    1. Ovary wall and seed coat are *fused*   **achene***

    2. Ovary wall hard or woody but *can be separated* from the seed   **nut**

  B. Fruits with **two to many seeds**

    1. Ovary with *several cavities* (seen when cut in cross section) and several to many seeds   **capsule**

    2. Ovary with *one cavity*

      a) Mature ovary opens along *both sides*   **legume**

      b) Mature ovary opens along *one side*   **follicle**

II. Fleshy fruits

  A. Ovary with **one seed**, which is surrounded by a very *hard stone*   **drupe**

  B. Ovary with **many seeds**; *does not have a "stone"*

    1. All of mature ovary tissue is soft and fleshy   **berry****

    2. Ovary wall seen as "core" around seed   **pome**

Achene

Nut

Capsule

Legume

Follicle

Drupe

Berry

Pome

* In the grass family, an achene is called a **grain** (rice, wheat)

** Berries of some families have special names: citrus family = **hesperidium**

                                                  squash family = **pepo**

Examples:

Nuts -   Walnuts
Capsule -   Okra
Legume -   Green Bean
Follicle -   Milk Weed
Drupe -   Cherry, Peach, Plum
Berry -   Tomato
Hesperidium - Orange, Lemon, Grapefruit
Pepo -   Squash, Pumpkin
Pome -   Apple, Pear

_____
Last Name, First Name

Review Questions

22. What is the more specific name for the fibroblasts in reticular connective tissue?

23. What does the fat droplet do to the organelles in a fat cell?

24. What is the name of the fibroblasts found in cartilage connective tissue?

25. Exactly where is the yellow bone marrow found in compact bone?

26. Where are the male and female gametes found in a flower?

27. How does a pine tree and other conifers adapt for living where the growing season is very short?

28. Where is the greatest plant diversity found?

29. What are the differences between pollination and fertilization?

Skeleton

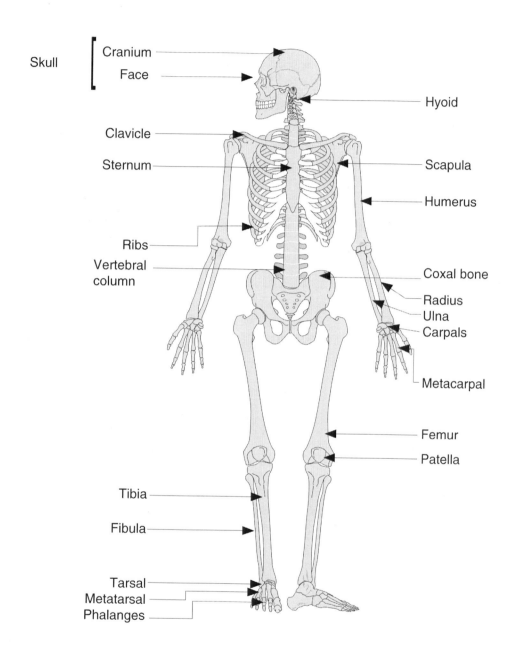

Skull [Cranium

Face

Hyoid

Clavicle

Sternum

Scapula

Humerus

Ribs

Vertebral
column

Coxal bone

Radius

Ulna

Carpals

Metacarpal

Femur

Patella

Tibia

Fibula

Tarsal
Metatarsal
Phalanges

The human skeleton consists of an **Axial Skeleton** and an **Appendicular Skeleton**.

Skeletal System: Axial Skeleton

14

Skeletal System

Generalities - Osteology is the study of bones

The skeleton is divided into **two parts: the axial skeleton and the appendicular skeleton.** (see page 91)

1. The **axial skeleton** consists of the bones that form the axis of the body: **the head, the neck** and the **trunk.** More specifically, this includes the **skull** (with both the facial and cranial bones, and the auditory ossicles), the **hyoid**, the **vertebrae** (vertebral column) and the **ribs** and **breast bone** (thoracic cage).

2. The **appendicular skeleton** consists of the bones of the **upper and lower extremities and the girdles** which attach these extremities to the axial skeleton. The **upper extremities** include the **arms, and the pectoral girdle** which is the shoulder. The **lower extremities** are the **legs and the pelvic girdle** which is the hip.

There are **206 bones** in the body (we won't be studying all of them). We will start with the **axial skeletal system.**

Functions of the bones:

1. Give **shape and form** to the body.

2. Provide a framework for **support**. For example, the lower limbs support the trunk while standing.

3. **Protection**: the skull bones are **fused together** and enclose the brain, the vertebrae surround the spinal cord, and the rib cage protects the organs in the thorax: heart, lungs and great vessel.

4. **Movement**: the bones are used as **levers** onto which the muscles are attached. Many types of movements are possible thanks to the joints. This set-up allows us to walk, grasp, etc.

5. **Store minerals** such as **calcium and phosphates**, forming calcium phosphate which is called **hydroxyapatite**. Both of these mineral salts account for the **hardness** of the bones and they may also be released into the blood if other parts of the body are in deficit.

6. **Blood cell formation**: Recall, previously we learned that **spongy bone** contains the **red bone marrow** and **compact bone** contains the **yellow bone marrow** (which is found in the medullary cavities of long bones). The red bone marrow produces **RBC, WBC,** and **platelets**. This production is called **hematopoiesis**. About **one million RBC** are produced per second to replace the worn out RBC which are destroyed in the liver. In **adults**, the only **active red bone marrow** is found in the head of the femur, the head of the humerus, the vertebrae, the pelvis and in the diploe of flat bones. The rest of the spongy bone as well as the yellow marrow could turn into active red marrow if the individual needs to increase RBC production like in a condition called **Anemia**. This is in contrast to a new born infant in which, active red marrow is found in all spongy bones as well as in the medullary cavities.

Classification of Bones

1. **Long bones** have an **elongated shape** and they are longer than they are wide. Therefore, long does not mean large bones necessarily. Long bones have a **shaft and two ends**. They are made up primarily of **compact bone** however; the interior portions of their ends consist of spongy bone. Long bones act as **levers**. Examples of long bones: all the bones of the limbs which include the femur, humerus, radius, ulna, tibia and fibula. In addition, the bones in the palm of your hand, the metacarpals and the bones in the sole of your foot, the metatarsals are also long bones. So are the bones found in the digits of your hands and feet and they are called the phalanges.

2. **Short bones** are **cube shaped** and consist mostly of **spongy bone**. These bones are the small bones of the wrist (carpals) and the bones in the ankle (tarsals). There is a particular type of short bone called a **sesamoid bone**. This is simply a short bone embedded in a tendon like the **kneecap (patella)**. Some individuals develop additional sesamoid bones in certain tendons due to repeated movements.

3. **Flat bones** are **thin with a slight curve** and a broad surface. These bones serve to **protect** the underlying organs. Their exterior and interior surfaces are made of up a thin layer of compact bone and then there is a layer of spongy bone sandwiched between these two surfaces. Some examples of flat bones are the sternum, ribs, and most of the skull bones.

4. **Irregular bones** have a **variety of shapes** and are more complex. They are made up of **spongy** bone in varying amounts which is enclosed by a thin compact layer. Examples of irregular bones are the vertebrae, pelvis and some of the facial bones.

The following pictures illustrate the **directional terms** frequently used in anatomy:

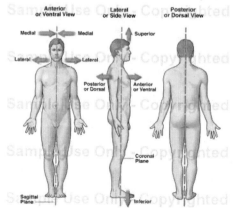

Superior Skull

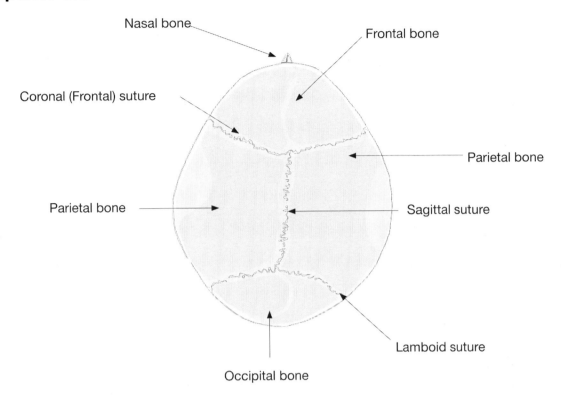

Nasal bone

Frontal bone

Coronal (Frontal) suture

Parietal bone

Parietal bone

Sagittal suture

Lamboid suture

Occipital bone

Posterior Skull

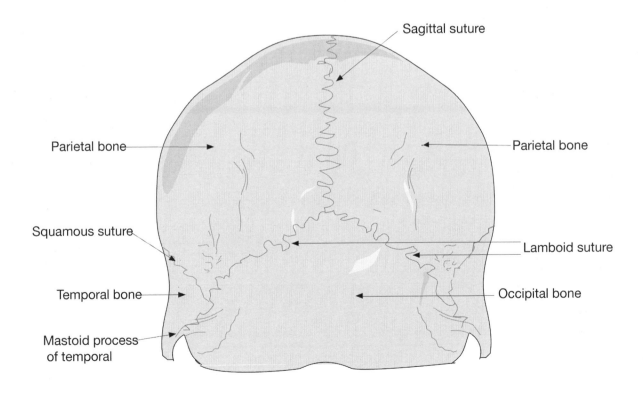

Sagittal suture

Parietal bone

Parietal bone

Squamous suture

Lamboid suture

Temporal bone

Occipital bone

Mastoid process
of temporal

Lateral View of Skull

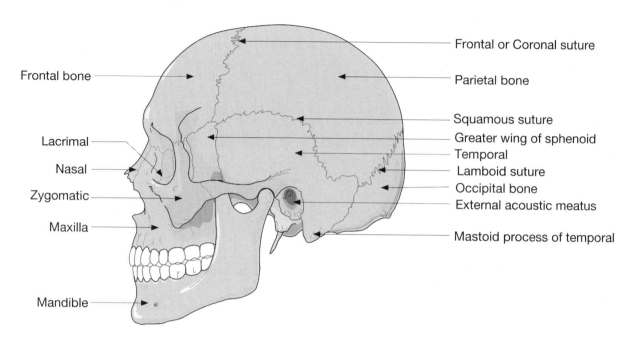

Frontal bone

Lacrimal

Nasal

Zygomatic

Maxilla

Mandible

Frontal or Coronal suture

Parietal bone

Squamous suture
Greater wing of sphenoid
Temporal
Lamboid suture
Occipital bone
External acoustic meatus

Mastoid process of temporal

Floor of Cranial Cavity (Base)

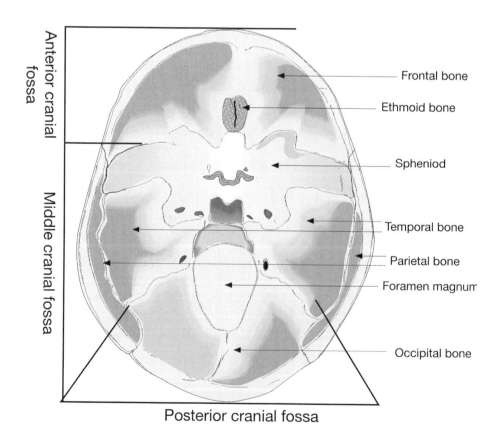

Anterior cranial fossa

Middle cranial fossa

Posterior cranial fossa

Frontal bone

Ethmoid bone

Spheniod

Temporal bone

Parietal bone

Foramen magnum

Occipital bone

Ethmoid bone

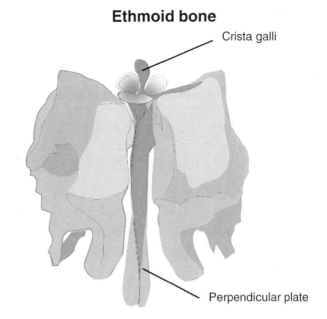

Crista galli

Perpendicular plate

Sphenoid bone

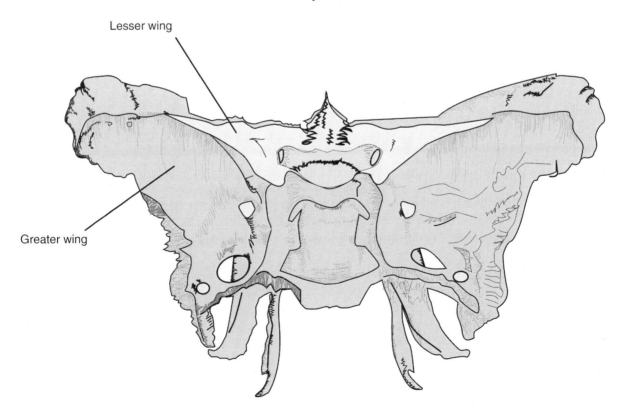

Lesser wing

Greater wing

Axial Skeleton

Features of the Skull Bones: Cranial, Facial, and Auditory Ossicles

1. There are **28 bones** in the skull and they are divided into the **facial bones, cranial bones and the auditory ossicles**. The skull in its entirety appears like a boney lopsided sphere. It has a very complex structure and consists of both flat and irregular bones.

2. With the exception of the mandible and the auditory ossicles, all the skull bones are firmly united by **interlocking joints** called **sutures**. The bones which fuse together have serrated edges. The sutures between the flat bones of the skull have names: **coronal, sagittal, lamboid and squamous**. Locate these sutures on the diagrams provided in APB.

3. **Fontanelles** - these are areas in the skull they have not yet ossified so they are only found in infants. They are located at the intersection of the cranial bones and are soft areas.

4. **Cavities**: There are two **auditory** (ear) cavities on either side of the skull. Anteriorly, there is a **nasal** cavity, two **orbital** (eye) cavities and an **oral or bucal** cavity.

5. **Sinuses** - these are **air filled spaces** found inside of some bones. They serve to lighten the skull. Those that are situated around the nasal cavity are called the **paranasal** sinuses. Specific examples are the frontal and maxillary sinuses.

6. **Openings**: there are **85** openings in the skull. The most important ones are those that provide entrance for the nerves and major blood vessels. There are three types of openings:

   a) **Foramens** are round or oval openings

   b) **Canals** are pathways

   c) **Fissures** are narrow slit-like openings

Cranial Bones

The CRANIAL BONES make up the cranium. These bones enclose and protect the brain, house the hearing and equilibrium organs, and serve as attachment points for the muscles of the head. The cranium is light weight but very strong. It is divided into the **Vault** or skull cap and the **Base** or floor. Eight bones are involved. The vault is the top, sides, front and back of the skull. The bones that make up the vault are the **frontal, parietal, occipital and temporal**. The **base** is the floor of the skull and we may view it from the interior or the exterior. If the vault is removed, we may view the base from the inside. In fact, we see two prominent ridges which divide the base into three steps or **fossae** (shallow depressions). They are named the **anterior fossa, the middle fossa and the posterior fossa** (see page 76). The brain fits snugly into these three fossae and is then covered by the vault. The bones which comprise the base also include the **frontal, occipital and temporal plus the sphenoid and the ethmoid**. All of these may be seen when we look at the interior floor of the base. Exteriorly we can only see the occipital bone.

The **frontal bone** is the forehead; it forms the superior margins of the orbital cavities. The superior border fuses with the two parietal bones forming the coronal suture.

The **two parietal bones** form the bulk of the vault and meet each other at the saggital suture.

The **occipital bone** is behind the two parietal bones (lamboidal suture). This bone forms the base of the skull and has a large hole in it called the **foramen magnum**. This is where the brain stem (medulla oblongata) enters the skull. At the back of the head (exterior part of the occipital bone) one can feel a bump. This is called the **external occipital protuberance** and serves as an attachment point for muscles. This is an **anatomical landmark** on the surface of the body which we can "palpate" (feel).

The **two temporal bones** are on the lateral portions of the skull. They form the squamosal suture where they meet with the parietal bones. This area is the first part of the scalp to turn grey and since grey hair is a sign that time has passed it was named the temporal bone which means time. This bone houses the hearing and equilibrium apparatuses which are located deep inside the auditory canal.

The **sphenoid bone** has a butterfly shape. Notice that it has wings and feet. This bone is situated behind the nose and its wings make up the back walls of the orbital cavities. Since it makes contact with all the other cranial bones it is a keystone bone because it holds everything together. This bone is easily understood when it is removed from the skull however, inside the skull very little of it is visible.

The **ethmoid bone** is very delicate and is located in front of the sphenoid bone between the orbital cavities just behind the nasal cavity. It is the deepest bone of the skull.

Cranium: Bones in each of its components:

    Vault: frontal, parietal, occipital, temporal

    Base: frontal, occipital, temporal, sphenoid, ethmoid

Skull

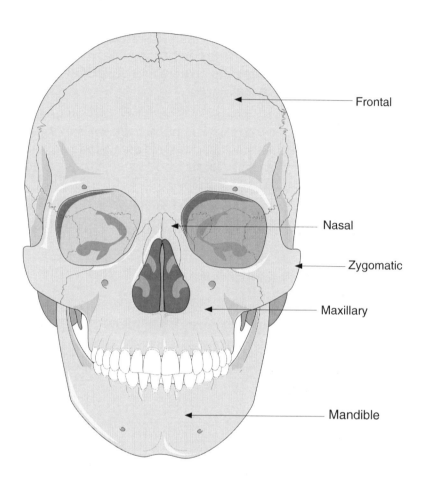

Frontal

Nasal

Zygomatic

Maxillary

Mandible

Facial Bones

The FACIAL BONES form the framework of the face. They provide cavities for the eyes, nose and mouth. They also secure the teeth and anchor the muscles of facial expression. There are 14 facial bones however, we will only discuss 10 of them. Generally, men have more elongated facial skeletons and women have rounder faces.

The **mandible** is the lower jaw and is where the lower teeth are anchored. It is the largest facial bone. On the medial surface of each ramus, one notes the **mandibular foramina**. This is the site where the dentist would inject Novocain to prevent pain while working on the lower teeth. Under the chin, one can palpate (touch) a slight indentation. This is called the **mandibular symphysis** and designates where the two halves of the mandible fused during embryological development. The **temporo-mandibular joint** (TMJ) is where the ramus of the mandible articulates (joins) with the temporal bone. This articulation (joint) is involved with chewing movements.

The **maxillary bones** are paired and make up the upper jaw so they house the upper teeth. If you use your tongue to touch the roof of your mouth or the **hard palate** one feels the horizontal portion of the maxillary bone. If the hard palate of the left maxillary bone does not completely fuse with the hard palate of the right maxillary bone, one would have an opening in the palate. This condition is called **cleft palate**. Since this is a developmental error in this location, it is usually associated with **cleft lip** (in which the two sides of the lip do not completely unite). These conditions affect speech and swallowing because food could go upwards into the nasal cavity and then down to the lungs. However, at one to two years of age, it may be surgically repaired with excellent results.

The **two nasal bones** form the bridge of your nose.

The **two zygomatic bones** are the check bones. They also form the inferior border of the orbital cavities.

The **lacrimal bones** are tiny bones found in the lower medial portion of each orbital cavity. These bones house the lacrimal sacs which are where the tears are produced. Unless you want to stick your fingers into your eyes, causing damage these bones may not be palpated.

The **vomer** forms the posterior part of the nasal septum which is what separates the nasal cavity in half.

Auditory Ossicles

There are three tiny bones inside each ear canal (deep inside of the temporal bones, in what is referred to as the middle ear). These bones are the smallest bones of the body. The **malleus** which means hammer secures itself onto the ear drum (tympanic membrane). The **incus** or anvil is located in the middle of the other two ossicles. The **stapes** or stirrup is inserted onto the oval window of the inner ear. These bones function to transfer and amplify sound impulses to the inner ear where the hearing receptors are located. Sound impulses from the environment reach the tympanic membrane which is like a drum and will vibrate. Since the malleus is attached to the tympanic membrane, this causes the auditory ossicles to move, and the stapes will push inwards against the fluid found on the other side of the oval window. The fluid then circulates inside the inner ear and stimulates the hearing receptors there which then transmit the signals to the brain to interpret the sound.

Hyoid

This is a U-shaped bone found in the neck and above the voice box (Adam's apple). You can feel it but it is a strange sensation. This bone is suspended by ligaments and the back of the tongue is attached to it.

Sacrum and Coccyx

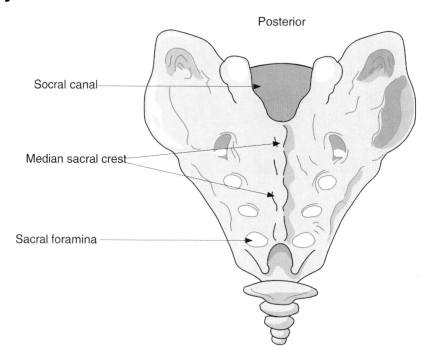

Posterior

Socral canal

Median sacral crest

Sacral foramina

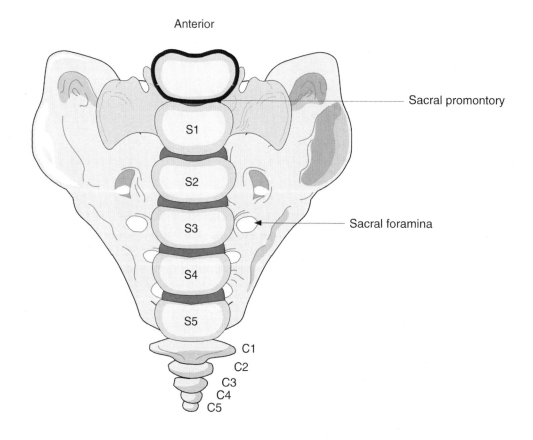

Anterior

Sacral promontory

S1

S2

S3 — Sacral foramina

S4

S5

C1
C2
C3
C4
C5

Vertebral Bones

The vertebral column is commonly called the spine or backbone. It consists of 26 irregular bones and provides a flexible curved structure. The column **functions** to:

1. provide support for the trunk and skull.

2. surround and protect the spinal cord

3. provide attachment points for the ribs and back muscles

There are 26 moveable vertebrae: **7 cervical, 12 thoracic, 5 lumbar, 1 sacrum** which articulates with the pelvis, and **1 coccyx** which is the terminal portion of the column and is very tiny.

The vertebrae are separated from one another by **intervertebral discs**. These discs are made of **fibrocartilage** and function to:

1. act as a cushioning pad so that if you jump up and down the individual vertebrae don't smash into one another

2. act as a shock absorber

3. hold the vertebrae together

4. allow the spine to flex and extend during walking or running

If you bend too far forward holding a heavy object this may cause the compression of one or more discs. The disc could even herniate or protrude and press on a spinal nerve causing severe pain. This is referred to as a **herniated disk**.

There are several **ligaments** which form a system of cables which keeps the column standing. These ligaments will also prevent you from bending too far forward, called **hyperflexion**. If you bend too far backwards these ligaments prevent **hyperextension**.

In the average adult, the column is 28 inches long. When viewed from the side, four curvatures may be observed. These curvatures cause the column to have an S shape and therefore, enable it to function like a spring giving flexibility to the spine:

The **cervical curvature** is concave posteriorly.

The **thoracic curvature** is convex posteriorly.

The **lumbar curvature** is concave posteriorly.

The **sacral curvature** is convex posteriorly.

Malformations of the Vertebral Column (Abnormal Curvatures)

Scoliosis is an abnormal lateral thoracic curvature and affects breathing.

Kyphosis or hunchback is an exaggerated thoracic curvature seen in the elderly due to osteoporosis.

Lordosis is an accentuated lumbar curvature due to pregnancy or a beer belly.

Sternum

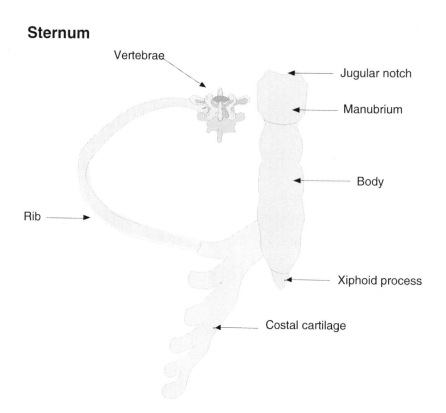

Vertebrae

Jugular notch

Manubrium

Body

Rib

Xiphoid process

Costal cartilage

Vertebra

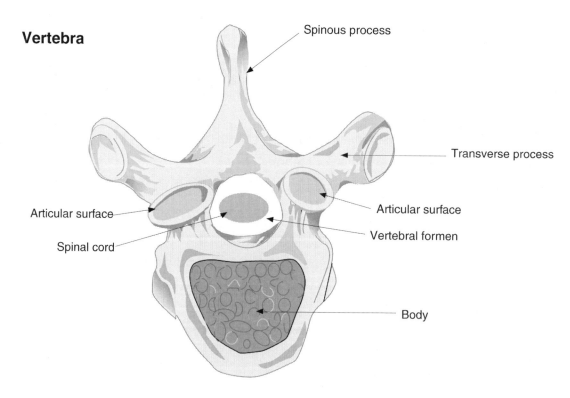

Spinous process

Transverse process

Articular surface

Articular surface

Spinal cord

Vertebral formen

Body

General Structure of Vertebrae

Note: **C1 (first cervical vertebrae)** is called the **atlas** and it is just a ring with no body. The skull sits atop this vertebrae and the articulation that forms between the occipital condyles and the articular surfaces of C1 allow us to nod to indicate YES.

C2 is called the **axis** and has a perpendicular tooth that sticks upwards into C1. Think of it as the missing body of C1. The articulation of the tooth or dens with C1 acts as a pivot point and allows you to turn your head from left to right to indicate NO. If one has a head-on car crash the dens could be forced up into the brain stem and damage the vital centers (i.e.: respiratory center) which would result in sudden death.

The spinous process of **C7** may be palpated. It is the bump felt at the back of the lower part of your neck and called the **vertebrae prominens**. Since we can locate it, it is also considered an anatomical landmark.

The spinal processes of the lumbar vertebrae may be seen on the back of an individual when he or she bends over. These particular spinous processes have a hatchet shape.

Thorax (Thoracic Cage)

The thorax is delineated dorsally by the thoracic vertebrae, laterally by the ribs, and anteriorly by the sternum (breast bone) and the costal cartilages (which are made up of hyaline cartilage and secure the ribs to the sternum). The thorax protects the heart, lungs, and great vessels like the aorta. The spaces between one rib and the next are called the intercostals spaces and contain the muscles of breathing. These muscles extend between two adjacent ribs.

Sternum (Breast Bone)

This is a flat bone about 6 inches long. At the top you can see and feel an indentation which is called the **jugular notch**. This is where the carotid artery branches off from the aorta. The sternum is made of three parts. The superior portion is shaped like a shield or necktie and is called the **manubrium**. The middle portion is the longest part and is called the **body** of the sternum. The inferior portion is shaped like a sword so it is pointy. This is called the **xiphoid process** (see page 104) and it attaches to the diaphragm.

Ribs

There are 12 pairs of ribs. Numbers 8, 9, 10, 11 and 12 are called the **false ribs** because they do not attach directly to the sternum as the upper 7 do. 8, 9 and 10 all converge onto number 7. Numbers 11 and 12 are further designated the **floating ribs** because they do not attach anteriorly to the sternum. They are shorter than the rest; do not reach around to join the sternum. Instead they wind up embedded in the muscles.

Costal Cartilage

The ribs are made of bone, however, they do not actually come all the way around to unite with the sternum. Actually, after the rib bends around the side of your body and starts to cross your chest at about midway is where the cartilage begins, connecting the ribs to the sternum.

Skeletal System: Appendicular Skeleton

15

Scapula—Posterior View

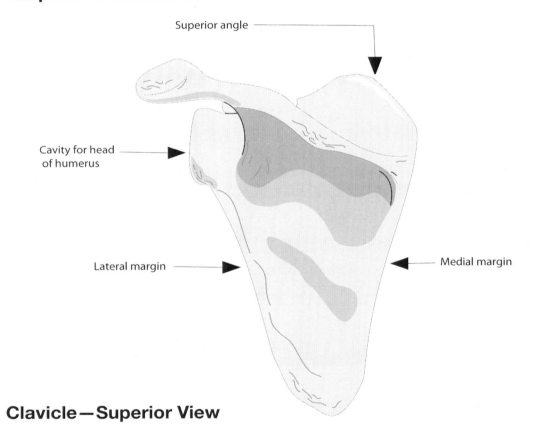

Superior angle

Cavity for head
of humerus

Lateral margin

Medial margin

Clavicle—Superior View

Articulates with sternum

Articulates with scapula

Humerus   # Femur

Anterior views

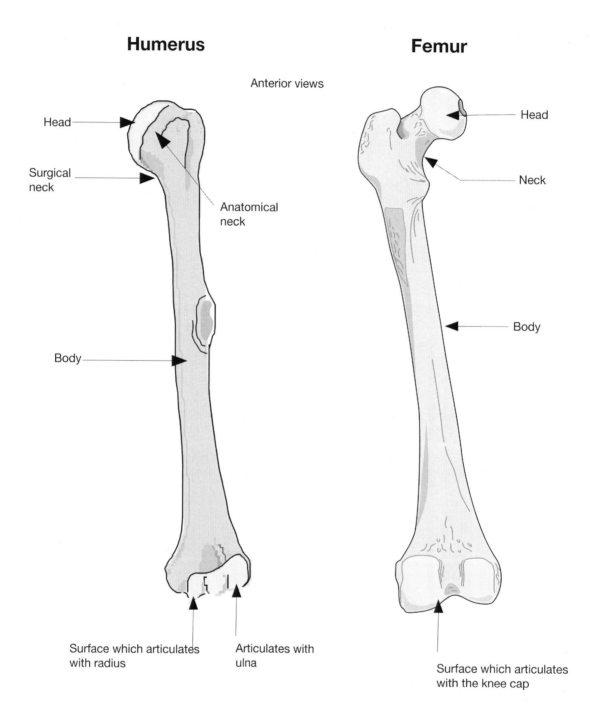

Head

Surgical
neck

Anatomical
neck

Head

Neck

Body

Body

Surface which articulates
with radius

Articulates with
ulna

Surface which articulates
with the knee cap

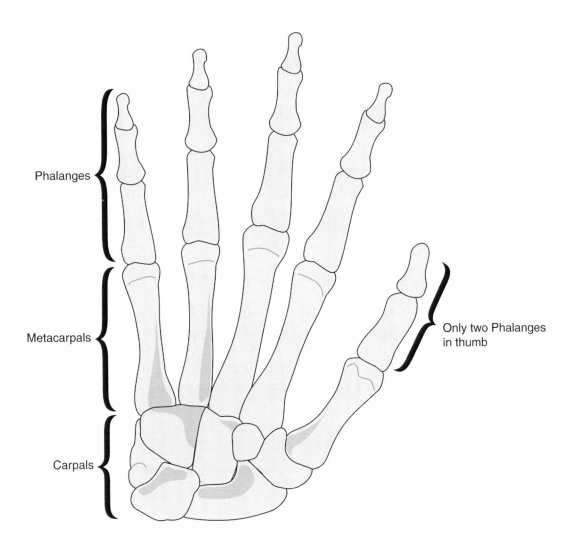

Phalanges

Metacarpals

Carpals

Only two Phalanges
in thumb

**Manus
(Hand)**

Appendicular Skeleton

The appendicular skeleton includes:

1. Pectoral girdle (shoulder), which attaches the upper limbs to the body

2. Pelvic girdle (hip), which secures the lower limbs

3. Limbs: each limb has three segments: arms, forearms, hands, and thighs, legs, feet.

I. PECTORAL GIRDLE

The clavicle, scapula and associated muscles make up the shoulder

Clavicle (collar bone) acts as an anterior brace. It becomes larger and stronger in body builders or in those who perform manual labor. It extends from the sternum to the scapula.

Scapula (shoulder blades) has a triangular or shovel-shape. It is attached to the thorax and column only by muscles.

II. UPPER LIMB

The upper limb is made up of the arm, forearm and hand.

The **brachium** (arm) is situated between the shoulder and elbow and contains the **humerus**. The head of the humerus fits into the scapula. The humerus has an **anatomical neck** which is just a slight constriction below the head. There is also a **surgical neck** which is the site that frequently fractures.

The **antebrachium** (forearm) contains the **radius and the ulna**. It is situated between the elbow and the hand. The elbow is a joint that is formed where the humerus meets the radius and the ulna.

The **radius** is on the lateral side of the forearm or it is on the thumb side.

To understand lateral and medial we must always refer to what is called the **anatomical position**. This is how you should picture the body when using words like medial and lateral or dorsal and ventral etc...And when you refer to something as right or left it is always with respect to the cadaver or model standing in the anatomical position. It is not your right or left but rather it is the right or left of the model. The anatomical position is when one stands fully **erect** with the **palms facing forward**, and the **feet pointing straight ahead**. For example, if you are looking at a model in the anatomical position, the heart is on the left and the liver is on the right. In other words, it is the model's left and right.

The **ulna** is a little longer than the radius.

The **manus** or hand has wrist bones called the **carpals**. These are the eight short bones in your wrist and there are 2 rows of them with 4 bones in each row. These bones give your wrist flexibility. Note that you do not really wear your "wrist" watch on your true wrist. Actually, you wear your watch on the distal ends of the radius and ulna. The true wrist is the proximal part of your hand.

The bones in the palm of your hand are called the **metacarpals** and there are five of them. These are considered long bones.

The bones in your fingers (digits) are called the **phalanges**. There are three phalanges in each finger except the thumb which only has 2 phalanges. Therefore, there are 14 phalanges and they are also long bones.

Pelivis – Anterior View

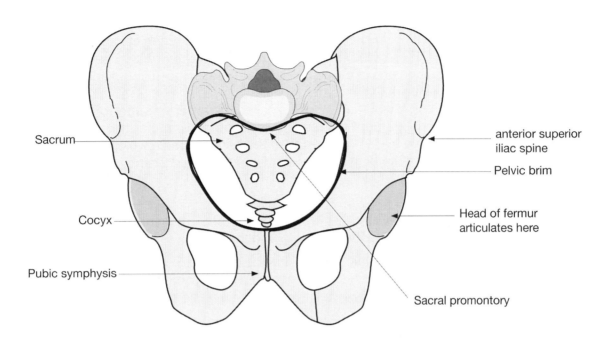

Sacrum

anterior superior
iliac spine

Pelvic brim

Cocyx

Head of fermur
articulates here

Pubic symphysis

Sacral promontory

Os Coxae - Lateral View

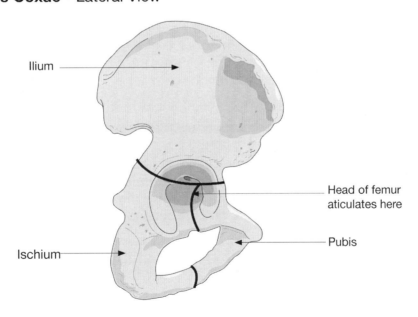

Ilium

Head of femur
aticulates here

Ischium

Pubis

III. PELVIC GIRDLE (Hip)

The pelvic girdle attaches the lower limbs to the axial skeleton. It supports the weight of the upper body and the organs. It is made of **two coxal bones** which unite anteriorly at the pubic arch. Posteriorly, they articulate with the **sacrum**. Each coxal bone is actually made of three fused bones called the **ilium, ischium and the pubis**. The bottom of the ischium is what you sit on and is called the **ischial tuberosity**. If you place your hands on your hips and extend you index finger forward along the hip you will feel a little point. This is another anatomical landmark and it is called the **anterior superior iliac spine**. From here, the **inguinal ligament** courses down to the pubic bone. The pelvic brim in a female is wider and more ovular in shape than the brim in a male which is more heart shaped. This is because the female body is adapted for child bearing.

IV. LOWER LIMB

The lower limb is made up of stronger bones because they must bear weight. Each limb is made of three segments: the thigh, the leg and the foot.

The thigh contains the **femur** which is the largest, longest and strongest bone in the body. You can not feel it because it is surrounded by bulky muscles. The femur articulates with the hip proximally. Distally with the tibia and patella.

The knee cap is called the **patella**. Recall, it is a sesamoid bone because it is inserted in the **quadriceps tendon**. The patella guards the knee joint.

The leg contains two parallel bones and they are called the **fibula and the tibia**. The tibia is the shin bone and next to the femur, it is the largest and strongest bone of the body. The fibula does not bear weight. These bones are both located between the knee and the ankle.

The foot functions to support our body weight and it acts like a lever to propel the body forward when we walk or run. The bones in the ankle are called the **tarsals** and there are seven of them. One of them, the heal bone is called the **calcaneus**. The tendon (**Achilles tendon**) of the calf muscle (which is called the gastrocnemius muscle) attaches to the back of the calcaneus. It is a common site of injury.

There are five **metatarsals** in the sole of the foot and 14 **phalanges**. Just like the hand, the toe digits all have three phalanges except for the big toe (hallux) which only has two. The metatarsals and tarsals are also long bones.

Throughout this material I have been indicating structures that you can feel on the surface of your body. These are what we call **anatomical landmarks** and serve as diagnostic features. For example, if you know where the manubrium meets the body of the sternum then this site allows you to find the second costal cartilage.

_____
Last Name, First Name

Review Questions

30. List all of the bones in the skull that are unpaired.

31. What is the bone disorder that frequently develops in the elderly?

32. Which bones make up the hard palate?

33. Which would be more debilitating, a compound fracture to the tibia or fibula?

34. What does the clavicle articulate with?

35. Where do you usually where your watch?

Reproduction: Male and Female

16

Reproduction

Outline:

1. Asexual

genes all from one parent

Types:

offspring are exact genetic copies of parent {

budding—i.e. hydra

fission—i.e. bacteria (This is the same as binary fission when one individual separates into two of about equal size.)

fragmentation & regeneration—i.e. sea stars

2. Sexual

fusion of 2 haploid sex cells (gametes) ⇒ diploid zygote (a combination of genes)

male gametes = sperm (cell w/flagellum, smallest cell in body)
female gametes = ovum (largest cell in body, nonmotile)

Hermaphroditism	—	non-motile animals
		solitary animals
		have both male and female reproductive systems

External Fertilization: fish, amphibians, aquatic invertebrates (Spawning is the release of eggs by a female organism and sperm by the male. This occurs in the water simultaneously to promote fertilization.)

Internal Fertilization: terrestrial animals
requires copulation
sophisticated reproductive systems
copulatory organs
structures to store sperm

Humans ducts and copulatory structures. The gonads contain the gametes:

♀ gonads = ovarie: gametes: ovum
♂ gonads = testes: gametes: sperm

Asexual Reproduction

Many invertebrates reproduce asexually by **budding**, the splitting off of new individuals from existing ones, for example the hydra. A bacterium undergoes **fission**, when one individual separates into two or more individuals of about equal size. The offspring of both budding and fission are exact genetic copies of the parent. Another method of asexual reproduction is **regeneration**, the breaking of the parent body into several pieces. Fragmentation must be accompanied by **regeneration**, the regrowth of body parts from pieces of an animal. If a sea star loses one of its arms, it will regenerate a new one in a matter of weeks. If the lost arm has at least 1/5 of the central disk attached to it, this arm can develop into a whole new organism, but this takes much longer. Fragmentation and regeneration also produces offspring which are exact genetic copies of the parent.

Sexual Reproduction: Female

After ovulation, the remaining **follicular tissue** grows within the ovary to form a solid mass called the **corpus luteum** (yellow body). The corpus luteum secretes **progesterone**, which prepares the uterus to receive and nourish a fertilized egg. **Progesterone**:

1. causes the uterine lining to thicken
2. causes the growth of many vessels into the lining
3. maintains the uterine lining during pregnancy if the egg is fertilized.

If the **egg is not fertilized**, the corpus luteum degenerates, and a new follicle matures during the next cycle.

Anatomical Structures in Female:

The **uterus** is the normal site of pregnancy. However, in about one out of 100 pregnancies, the embryo implants somewhere else, resulting in an **ectopic pregnancy** (out of place). Most ectopic pregnancies occur in the oviduct and are called **tubal pregnancies**. Ectopic pregnancies require surgical removal; otherwise, they can rupture surrounding tissues, cause severe bleeding and even death.

A thin membrane called the **hymen** partly covers the vaginal opening. With the first intercourse or vigorous physical activity it ruptures. The hymen has no known function.

Bartholin's glands are located near the vaginal opening. They secrete lubricating fluid during sexual arousal, as does the vaginal lining. This fluid also assists in preparing the vagina for the insertion of the male's penis.

The sole function of the **clitoris** is sexual arousal. It consists of a short shaft supporting a rounded **glans** or head, covered by a small hood of skin called the **prepuce**. The clitoris is like a tiny penis and is in fact, homologous to the male penis. During sexual arousal, the clitoris fills with blood. The glans has an enormous number of nerve endings and is very sensitive to touch. Gentle stimulation of the glans can often trigger orgasm. Some ancient cultures still carry out the practice of removing the female clitoris since they feel it has nothing to do with producing children. This is procedure is called a **clitorectomy**.

Hormones and the Cyclic Changes:

From puberty to about 50 years of age, about every 28 days, **FSH** (follicle stimulating hormone) is released from the pituitary gland in the brain to stimulate one of the dormant follicles to develop. Another hormone called **LH** (luteinizing hormone) triggers **ovulation** and the formation of the **corpus luteum** from the ruptured follicle. **Prolactin** is a hormone released from the anterior pituitary gland. It stimulates the breast tissue to promote milk secretion after birth.

The cyclic events that occur about every 28 days in the ovary are called the **ovarian cycle**. The related events in the uterus are called the **menstrual cycle**. The first day of a woman's period is designated as day 1 of the menstrual cycle. From the first day of the period until the first day of the next menstrual period is about 28 days on the average. Some women have 25 day cycles, others have 35 day cycles. Some women have what are called **irregular cycles** because the time between periods is a different length each month.

During **menstruation**, the thickened **endometrium** (inner lining of the uterus) breaks down and leaves the body through the vagina. The menstrual discharge, called the **menstrual fluid** consists of blood (since the blood vessels close up and break), endometrial cells and mucus. After menstruation, the endometrium grows again in preparation for the next pregnancy. The endometrium will thicken again through the time of ovulation, reaching a maximum at about 28 days. If an embryo has not implanted in the uterine lining by this time, menstruation begins again, marking the start of the next ovarian and menstrual cycle.

Cancer

Cancer may occur in any part of the female reproductive system. Doctors recommend that women have a yearly pelvic examination to detect cancers early. The earlier cancer is caught, the more successful the treatment. During this exam a **Pap test** is preformed, which involves removing cells from the cervix and then testing them for cancer. Women should also get in the habit of checking their breasts for lumps and other abnormalities on a monthly basis. Doctors recommend yearly mammograms (an X-ray of the breast) beginning at about age 30.

Female Anatomy

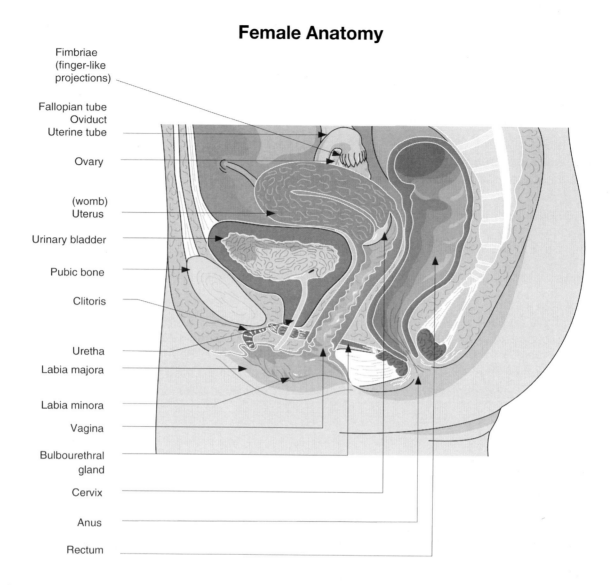

Fimbriae (finger-like projections)
Fallopian tube
Oviduct
Uterine tube
Ovary
(womb) Uterus
Urinary bladder
Pubic bone
Clitoris
Uretha
Labia majora
Labia minora
Vagina
Bulbourethral gland
Cervix
Anus
Rectum

Multiple Births

Fraternal or dizygotic twins develop when two separate eggs are ovulated and subsequently fertilized.

After the sperm fertilizes the egg, a zygote forms which will start dividing exponentially forming different types of developmental structures. If this structure in its early stages separates, **identical or monozygotic twins** result. If this splitting is not complete, **conjoined or Siamese twins** may develop.

Fertilization

The **oocyte** is viable for about one day (average) after ovulation while the sperm is viable for about 5 days (average) after ejaculation. Therefore, for fertilization to occur, **coitus** must be no more than 5 days before ovulation and no later than one day after ovulation.

24 hours after ovulation, the oocyte makes its way **one third** of the way down the length of the **uterine tube** (or **Fallopian tube** or **oviduct**) in its journey towards the uterus. If fertilization occurs, it also happens at this time in the upper third of the oviduct.

Three to four days after ovulation, if fertilization occurs, the zygote reaches the uterus.

Seven days after ovulation, if fertilization occurs **implantation** begins.

Unfertilized Egg

Two layers of cells surround the unfertilized egg: the outer most layer is called the **corona radiata**. It consists of two or three layers of cells, which serve as a protective coating. The corona is attached to a second layer, which is also for protection and is located underneath called the **zona pellucida**. The pellucida supplies proteins to the egg cell. For fertilization to occur, sperm cells rely on hyaluronidase (**acrosomal enzyme**) to disperse the corona radiata from the zona pellucida, thus permitting entry of one sperm cell, allowing it to contact the nucleus of the oocyte. It takes the secretions of dozens of sperm to weaken the layer enough for one sperm to penetrate.

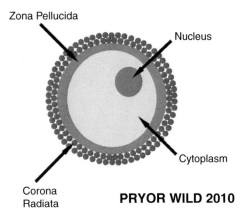

Zona Pellucida

Nucleus

Cytoplasm

Corona Radiata

PRYOR WILD 2010

Summary

- A female is born with 40,000 - 400,000 follicles

- The follicles are contained in the ovaries (almond shape, 1")

- When a follicle matures it releases one egg. This occurs every 28 days = **Ovulation**

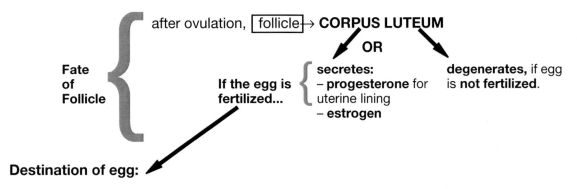

after ovulation, follicle → **CORPUS LUTEUM**

OR

Fate of Follicle

If the egg is fertilized...

secretes:
– **progesterone** for uterine lining
– **estrogen**

degenerates, if egg is **not fertilized**.

Destination of egg:

egg → oviduct (Fallopian tube) → egg becomes a zygote implanted in the endometrium of the uterus

(this is where **fertilization** occurs, in the upper third of uterine tube)

If fertilization doesn't occur—**menstruation occurs**

Embryo = the term used to refer to the zygote until the 9th week

Fetus = the term used to refer to the developing organism form the 9th week until the birth

Anatomy:

- uterus

- cervix = neck of uterus

- vagina:

function: 1. birth canal

2. to accomodate male penis. The vagina elongates to accomodate the erect penis. If the penis is long enough, it may reach the cervix which is the neck of the uterus. This is known as "bottoming out" and may be painful for a female during coitus.

structures: labia minora

labia majora

hymen

- Bartholin's glands

- clitoris—sexual arousal

glans

prepuce

Sexual Reproduction: Male

Hormones, Glands and Sperm:

The male secretes the same hormones as a female from the pituitary gland in the brain (FSH and LH), only they cause different responses. Both hormones act on the **testes** which are housed outside the abdominal cavity. The testes are located in a sac called the **scrotum. Sperm** need a cooler environment to develop properly therefore, the testes are located outside the body. When it is too cold outside the male testes are brought upwards towards the warmer body by the **cremaster muscle**. This muscle courses through the spermatic cord. The **dartos muscle** lines the scrotum. It also contracts when it is too cold which tends to shrivel up the testes.

FSH will increase **sperm** production in the testes while **LH** promotes the secretion of **testosterone** by the testes. **Testosterone** is the hormone resposible for the male secondary sexual characteristics (beard, facial hair, body hair, penis enlargement, etc). A sperm cell takes about two months to form during a process called **spermatogenesis**. This occurs in the coiled tubes of the testes called the **seminiferous tubules**. Next the sperm pass into the **epididymis** (a coiled tube) to mature (1 month). They become motile and are stored here until there is an ejaculation.

The male has **two bulbourethral glands** which secrete a few drops of fluid into the urethra during sexual arousal. They are called **Cowper's glands** and are situated at the base of the penis. This fluid is also known as **pre-ejaculate** and it helps lubricate the urethra, helping sperm move through it during an ejaculation. In addition, its serves to lubricate the vagina for coitus.

Semen is made up of the glandular secretions from the **prostate, seminal vesicles and the bulbourethral glands** (which together account for 95% of the fluid in the semen) plus the **sperm** (which accounts for only 5% of the fluid). But in this 5% there are from 200 - 500 million sperm, only one of which may fertilize an egg cell. The other sperm play an accessory role in fertilization, causing changes in the environment of the female reproductive tract.

Male Anatomy

The **glans** of the penis is richly supplied with nerve endings and is highly sensitive to stimulation. As in the female, a fold of skin called the **prepuce** or foreskin, covers the glans. **Circumcision** is the surgical removal of the prepuce and is commonly preformed for religious or health reasons at birth. Circumcised and uncircumcised penises look different but function in the same way. Males who haven't been circumcised should pull the foreskin back when they bathe to prevent a build up of secretions which cause irritation and odor.

The **male urethra** originates from the bladder and then passes through the prostate gland. Since this portion of the urethra goes through the prostate gland it is named the **prostatic urethra**. From here, the urethra passes over the pubic bone and is called the **diaphragmatic urethra**. Finally, the urethra reaches the base of the penis and continues to the head of the penis. Therefore, this portion is called the **penile urethra**. The male urethra is much longer than the urethra of the female.

Ejaculation

The process of **ejaculation** occurs in two stages:

1. **filling phase** - at the peak of sexual arousal, muscles in the epididymus, glands (bulbourethral, prostate, and seminal vesicles) and in the vas deferens contract. These contractions force the secretions (including the sperm) into the vas deferens and then propel it through the **ejaculatory duct** into the prostatic urethra. At the same time, a **sphincter** near the base of the bladder contracts, preventing urine from leaking into the urethra from the bladder. Another sphincter located on the distal side of the prostate gland (at the base of the penis) also contracts. These two contracted sphincters close off the prostatic urethra so that it fills with semen. Due to the fact that both sphincters are contracted at this point in time, the ejaculatory duct is the only route open for business. Therefore, there is a build up of semen in the prostatic urethra with no way out yet.

2. **expulsion phase** - Now the **sphincter** at the base of the penis relaxes (under voluntary control up to a point), allowing the semen to enter the penile urethra. Simultaneously, a series of strong muscle contractions around the base of the penis and along the urethra expel the semen out of the penis during orgasm.

Ejaculation can occur even while a man is sleeping. This is called **nocturnal emission** (wet dream) and is normal in adolescent and adult males due to hormonal fluctuations.

Inguinal hernia

Sometimes part of the intestine protrudes into the scrotum through a weakness in the abdominal wall. Inguinal hernias can be painful and usually require surgery to correct.

Cancer

Older men are more likely to get cancer of the **prostate gland**, which requires treatment.

Testicular cancer is cancer of the testes. It usually occurs in males between the ages of 15 and 35. If treated early, there is an excellent chance of cure. Men should also get into the habit of checking their testes to make sure there are no lumps or abnormalities.

Male Anatomy

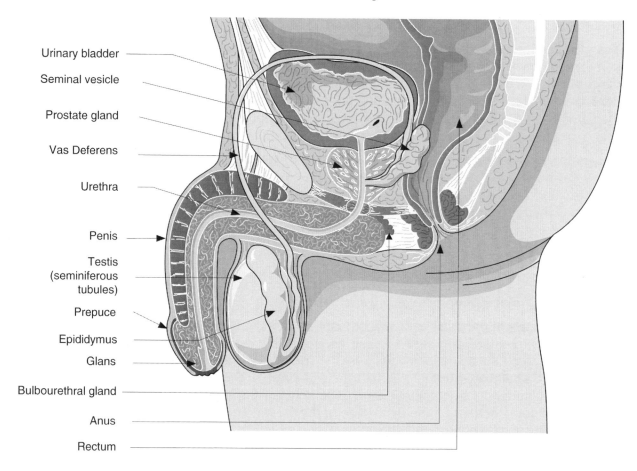

- Urinary bladder
- Seminal vesicle
- Prostate gland
- Vas Deferens
- Urethra
- Penis
- Testis (seminiferous tubules)
- Prepuce
- Epididymus
- Glans
- Bulbourethral gland
- Anus
- Rectum

Summary

Gonads = testes/testicles → millions of sperm produced daily from puberty to old age in scrotum

Regulatory hormones: The releasing hormones from the hypothalamus cause the secretion of **FSH** and **LH** from the pituitary gland.

Therefore, **r.h. FSH** and **r.h. LH** stimulate the release of FSH and LH which are made in the anterior pituitary gland. Both LH and FSH cause activity in the testes where they work. FSH causes the testes to make sperm. LH causes the testes to make **testosterone**.

hypothalamus (releasing hormones) → anterior pituitary gland

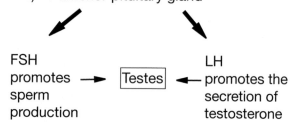

FSH promotes sperm production → Testes ← LH promotes the secretion of testosterone

Sperm Path:

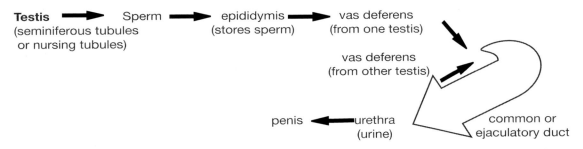

The vas deferens goes up through the spermatic cord into the abdomino-pelvic cavity.
Then it goes up and around to the back of the bladder. Here it meets the ejaculatory ducts.

Glands:

2 seminal vesicles—clear fluid, lubricates, and nourishes sperm

prostate—milky secretion which protects sperm

2 bulbourethral glands—fluid droplets during arousal

Semen: sperm + secretions = ejaculate (discharge fluid)
       5%   95%
(200-500 million sperm are contained in the 5%)

Penis:

erectile tissue - spongy tissue which fills with blood

shaft

glans—prepuce/circumcision

Human Sexual Response

Most female mammals in many species are receptive to males only on certain days (for example, dogs and cats). During these specific mating times the female is said to be in "heat" meaning she is at her peak of sexual readiness or also called **estrus**. This is the only time she ovulates and the only time her uterus is primed for implantation.

Humans and several other primates do not have distinct mating periods. Females are receptive to males throughout the year. In humans, sexual behavior is more than just a physical association to reproduce, it is more complex and our sexuality is also emotional. There are **four phases** involved in our sexual response and behavior.

Four Phases to the Sexual Response:

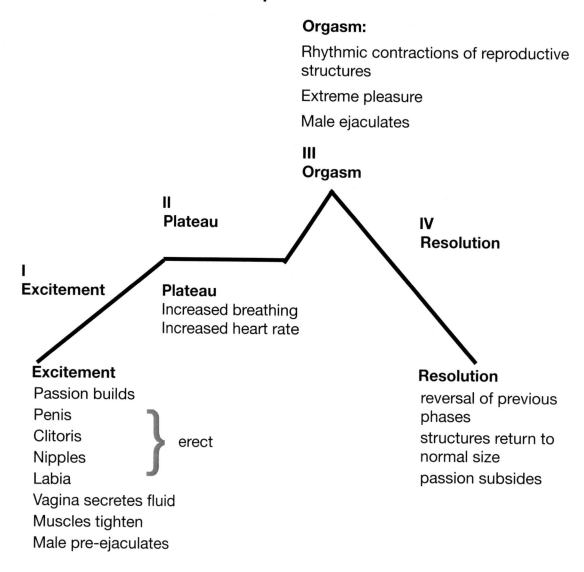

Orgasm:

Rhythmic contractions of reproductive structures

Extreme pleasure

Male ejaculates

III
Orgasm

II
Plateau

IV
Resolution

I
Excitement

Plateau
Increased breathing
Increased heart rate

Excitement
Passion builds
Penis
Clitoris
Nipples   } erect
Labia
Vagina secretes fluid
Muscles tighten
Male pre-ejaculates

Resolution
reversal of previous phases
structures return to normal size
passion subsides

Viagra (Sildenafil citrate)

Physiologically, **nitric oxide** is released locally during arousal into the **corpus cavernosum** (the erectile tissue) of the penis. Nitric oxide activates an enzyme called **cyclase** which causes an increase in another substance called **cGMP**. cGMP causes smooth muscle relaxation of the arteries that supply the penis with blood. So these arteries dilate and blood flows into the corpus cavernosum causing an erection. Normally, when the erection subsides it is due to a **diesterase** which causes the degradation of cGMP so the blood supply decreases. This is where **Viagra** comes in; it inhibits the degradation of the cGMP so that the blood keeps flowing into the penis. In other words, it prevents the diesterase from removing the cGMP.

Contraception

The most effective method of contraception is the **condom** and/or the **pill**. A **spermicide** is a contraceptive substance that helps eradicate sperm. Usually it is combined with other birth control methods. The **rhythm method** estimates a woman's likelihood of fertility (days 8-19) based on the previous menstrual cycle (days 1-7). The infertile period extends from days 20-30. This is not an effective method to prevent pregnancy.

Feline Dissection

17

I. Head and neck

Mandible—supports the lower teeth and is composed of two dentary bones united anteriorly at the mental (mandibular) symphysis.

Masseter muscle—enables the cat to chew. This muscle has essentially the same origins, insertions, and functions as those of the human.

Digastric muscle—serves to depress the lower jaw and is situated on the ventral border of the mandible.

Sternomastoid muscle—is named on the basis of its origin and insertion so it may be easily located. It contributes to the movement of the head.

Sternocleidomastoid muscle—is not found in the cat. In its place, the cat has the sternomastoid muscle and the cleidomastoid muscle, both of which turn the head.

Salivary glands—produce saliva, which moistens the food and aids the cat in swallowing.

II. Shoulder

Deltoid muscle—there are three in the cat compared to only one in humans. They flex and rotate the humerus and the forelimbs.

Latissimus dorsi muscle—pulls the arm in a caudodorsal direction.

III. Brachium

Biceps muscle—its origin is near the glenoid cavity (scapula) and the insertion is at the radial tuberosity. The function is to flex the forelimb and there is only one head to this muscle in the cat.

Triceps muscle—the origin of this muscle is located at the scapula and shaft of the humerus. Its insertion is located at the olecranon of the ulna. Its function is to extend the forelimb.

IV. Pectoral (chest) region

Pectoralis major muscle—its origin is at the sternum and it inserts at the pectoral ridge of the humerus. The function is to adduct the forelimbs.

V. Abdominal muscles

Rectus abdominis muscle—its origin is at the pubis and it inserts at the sternum. Its function is to constrict the abdomen. This muscle is a strap-like paired muscle located on either side of the linea alba.

Linea alba—separates the rectus abdominis muscles. It is a seam.

External abdominal oblique muscle—its origin is at the lumbdorsal fascia and ribs and it inserts in the linea alba and pubis. It also constricts the abdomen.

VI. Thigh region

Rectus femoris muscle—this muscle is one of the quadriceps, which comprise the anterior compartment of the thigh. These muscles are all powerful extensors of the knee. The rectus femoris' origin is located at the ilium and the insertion is located at the patella. Its function is to extend the femur.

Sartorius muscle—located on the anterior, inner thigh. It extends and rotates the leg.

Gracilis muscle—located on the posterior, inner thigh. This muscle adducts the leg.

Gluteus maximus muscle—its origin is at the sacral and caudal vertebrae and its insertion is at the greater trochanter of the femur. Its function is to abduct the thigh.

VII. Leg

Gastrocnemius muscle—The origin of this muscle is at the medial condyle of the femur. Its insertion is located on the surface of the calcaneus via Achille's tendon. Its function is plantar flexion of the foot and flexion of the leg at the knee.

VIII. Organs of the thoracic cavity

Larynx—provides entrance into the lower respiratory tract of the cat.

Trachea—made of individual C-shape cartilage rings that form and support its wall and keep this tubular passageway open. The trachea extends from the larynx to the bronchi.

Thymus—plays a key role in the immune system. It is located in the anterior thorax below the manubrium of the sternum.

Lung—each lung is positioned in a pleural cavity. The visceral pleura is the serous membrane that adheres to the lung; the parietal pleura is the serous membrane which lines the thoracic wall and thoracic surface of the diaphragm. The right lung consists of four chambers and the left consists of three lobes.

Heart—all mammals have a four-chambered heart that is remarkably similar. The heart has a caudally pointed apex and a broad base at the cranial end.

Diaphragm—is a large dome shaped muscle that forms the floor of the thoracic cavity.

IX. Abdominal-pelvic cavity

Esophagus—transports food and fluid from the pharynx to the stomach.

Liver—is a large, reddish-brown digestive gland, immediately caudal to the diaphragm.

Gallbladder—is a pear-like organ attached to the under side of the liver. It is where the bile is stored.

Stomach—receives food from the esophagus and mixes it with gastric juice. It has the appearance of a small pouch located on the left side of the body cavity immediately caudal to the diaphragm.

Spleen—a reddish-brown organ, which is dorsal and slightly to the left of the stomach.

Pancreas—is an elongate and lobular organ, which extends from the duodenum to the spleen. It produces the majority of the digestive enzymes in an inactive form as well as insulin and glucagon. Note that both the pancreatic duct and the common bile duct converge at the same place in the duodenum.

Small intestine—receives secretions from the liver and pancreas which, will break down food both chemically and mechanically. It then absorbs the nutrients, and passes the undigested materials to the large intestine. It is situated between the pyloric sphincter of the stomach and the ileocecal valve of the large intestine. It is divided into the duodenum, jejunum and the ileum.

Large intestine—forms and provides passage for the feces. It is responsible for the re absorption of water and certain electrolytes. It is the terminal portion of the tract and extends to the anus. Note that the cat lacks an appendix.

Greater omentum—is a fold of the peritoneal membrane, which covers the underlying viscera like an apron. It is attached to the convex border (greater curvature) of the stomach. It stores lipids and protects the viscera.

Kidneys—the kidneys of the cat have only one pyramid, while a human has six or more.

Ureters—tubes which transport urine from each kidney to the urinary bladder.

Urinary bladder—is a hollow, distensible, muscular organ where the urine is collected and stored.

X. Reproductive organs of the male cat

Ductus (vas) deferens—from each testis a vas deferens, various blood vessels and nerves pass up through the inguinal canal and then enter the urethra (near the prostate).

Urethra—carries urine from the bladder to the exterior through the penis. It is also a reproductive organ, which carries the semen.

Penis—is ventral to the testis.

Glans penis—the prepuce (foreskin) of the penis covers the glans penis.

Os penis (bacula)—the glans penis contains a small bone which facilitates the errection of the penis.

XI. Reproductive organs of the female cat

Ovaries—are small, whitish organs posterior to the kidneys where the ovum are produced and then released into the oviducts.

Uterus—is a Y-shaped muscular organ which consists of horns and a body.

Uterine horns—receive the uterine tubes (oviducts) and are the sites for implantation. They enable the cat to have large litters.

Body of uterus—the uterine horns unite medially to become the body of the uterus.

Vagina—is a muscular chamber between the body of the uterus and the urogenital sinus. The vagina is ventral to the anus and receives semen during copulation.

Urogenital sinus (vestibule)—is a common passageway formed by the union of the urethra and the vagina. It opens to the exterior as the urogenital aperture. Therefore, it is for both the urinary and reproductive systems.

Vulva—is comprised of the urogenital aperture, labia minor and the clitoris.

Cat Anatomy

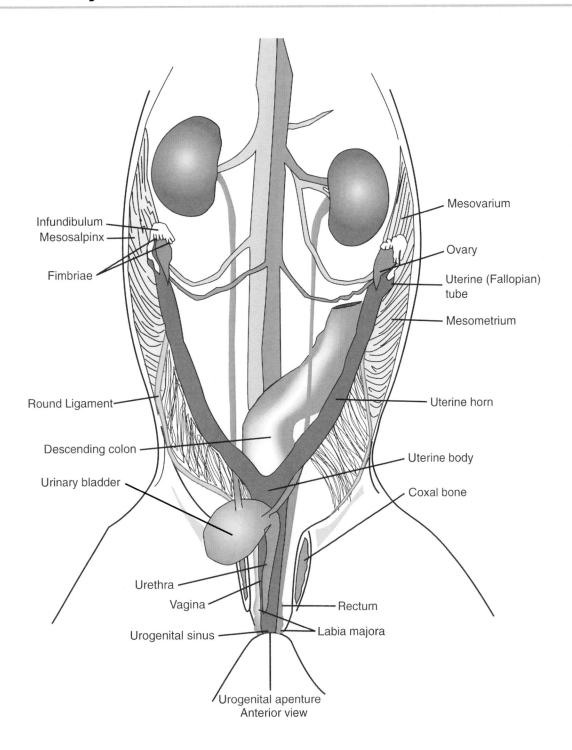

Infundibulum
Mesosalpinx
Fimbriae

Mesovarium

Ovary

Uterine (Fallopian) tube

Mesometrium

Round Ligament

Uterine horn

Descending colon

Uterine body

Urinary bladder

Coxal bone

Urethra
Vagina

Rectum

Urogenital sinus

Labia majora

Urogenital apenture
Anterior view

129

Muscles of the Human Body and Anabolic Steroids

18

Outline

I. Muscles of the Head

    a) Facial Expression

    b) Mastication

            Masseter

II. Anterior Neck and Throat

    a) Sternocleidomastoid

    b) Swallowing

            Digastric

            Sternohyoid

III. Muscles of the Abdominal Wall

        Exterior Abdominal Obliques

        Rectus Abdominis

IV. Superficial Muscles of the Thorax

    a) Anterior Thorax

            Pectoralis Minor

            Serratus Anterior

    b) Posterior Thorax

            Trapezius

V. Arm Movements

a) Pectoralis Major

b) Latissimus Dorsi

c) Deltoid

VI. Forearm Extensors and Flexors

a) Posterior: Triceps

b) Anterior: Biceps

VII. Thigh

a) Anterior

  Quadriceps

  Rectus Femoris

  Lateral, Medial and Intermediate Vastus

b) Posterior

  Hamstrings

  Gluteus Maximus

  Gluteus Medius

  Gluteus Minimus

c) Medial

  Gracilis

VIII. Leg (Ankle and Toe Movements)

Posterior and Superficial

Gastrocnemius

Muscles - the details

There are over 600 muscles in the body. To learn the muscles requires an understanding of all body movements. Muscles are grouped by function and by location, usually from head to foot. We will only look at a few of them and discuss only the ones on the surface of the body which are called the superficial muscles.

Flexion

When a muscle is flexed, the angle of the joint is decreased. For example, when the biceps muscle is flexed, the forearm is brought closer to the upper arm and the angle at the elbow decreases.

Abduction

This is a motion that pulls a structure away from the midline of the body.

Adduction

This is a motion that pulls a structure towards the midline of the body. For example, to stay seated in the saddle while horseback riding, one adducts the thigh muscles so the legs hug the sides of the horse or are brought closer together towards each other.

Atrophy

When a muscle decreases in size and starts to waste away because it is not being used. An example is when a cast is left on a body part or extended bed rest. Atrophy can usually be reversed with exercise.

I. Muscles of the Head

  a) **Muscles of Facial Expression**: we use these muscles everyday because they reflect the mood we are in. For example, if you smile you would be using some of the muscles of the face to make that expression. Another example is when you whistle because you use other muscles in the face. One of these muscles is called the **Frontalis**, which is located in your forehead and you would use it when you squint.

  b) **Muscles of Mastication**: mastication means chewing. One of the muscles involved with chewing is called the **Masseter** and it elevates the mandible (jaw).

II. Muscles of the Anterior Neck and Throat

  a) **Sternocleidomastoid (SCM)**: this muscle is a large muscle found in the neck and it is used as a landmark which divides the neck into an anterior triangle and a posterior triangle. The SCM extends from the sternum and clavicle to the mastoid process (the rounded bump you feel behind your ear) of the temporal bone. If you examine the name of this muscle it indicates its origin and insertion. "Sterno" means the sternum, "cleido" indicates the clavicle, and of course the word "mastoid" is the mastoid process of the temporal bone.

  b) **Muscles involved with Swallowing**

   1. **Digastric**: this muscle is found in the neck and extends from the angle of the mandible to the hyoid bone. The midline of this muscle is held in place by a tendon. The digastric muscle consists of two bellies and its function is to open the mouth.

2. **Sternohyoid**: this muscle is also a neck muscle and as its name implies, it extends from the sternum to the hyoid bone. Since it is below the hyoid bone it is considered an infrahyoid muscle. Its function is to depress the hyoid bone as well as the larynx after swallowing.

III. Muscles of the Abdominal Wall

a) **External Abdominal Oblique** make up the lateral abdominal wall. It helps compress the abdomen.

b) **Rectus Abdominus**: this is a long strap like muscle located in the anterior abdomen. It flexes the vertebral column and is a pillar of strength when one goes to lift weight. It extends from the pubis to the rib cage and the left side is separated from the right side by a seam called the **linea alba** (white line). Its inferior portion is delineated by the spermatic cord. When a man takes off his shirt you can see six segments of this muscle so it is commonly called the "six pack." Actually there are really eight segments to this muscle, because two of the segments are below the naval.

Both of these muscles (External oblique and Rectus) function to:

1. support and protect the viscera

2. flex and rotate the trunk

3. when these muscles are contracted, the intra-abdominal pressure increases which facilitates urination, defecation, birthing, vomiting, coughing, etc.

Rectus Abdominis - its inferior portion is delineated by the spermatic cord.

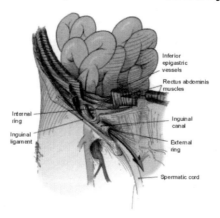

IV. Superficial Muscles of the Thorax

a) **Anterior thorax**

Pectoralis Minor: this muscle pulls the scapula forward and downward. Therefore, it is a muscle that acts on the pectoral girdle. It is considered to be a lesser chest muscle and can only be seen once the pectoralis major has been removed. The pectoralis major is not discussed here since it is involved in arm movements so we will see it in another section.

Serratus Anterior: this muscle lies deep and inferior to the pectoral muscles on the lateral rib cage. Therefore, it forms the wall of the arm pit (axilla). Its origins which are the ribs have a serrated or saw-tooth appearance. It functions to protract and hold the scapula against the chest wall.

b) **Posterior thorax**

Trapezius: this muscle is found on the back of the neck and it extends to the dorsum. The trapezius muscle has a trapezoid shape when you view the left side and right side together. It acts on the pectoral girdle and it elevates the scapula as well as stabilizing it. Basically, it braces the shoulder.

V. Muscles of the Posterior Shoulder (which are involved with arm movements)

a) **Pectoralis Major:** this is the largest chest muscle. It adducts the arm which means that it is used to bring the fully extended arm toward the body. Most importantly, it is used to flex the arm at the shoulder and would be the muscle used for throwing a ball.

b) **Latissimus Dorsi:** this is commonly called the "lats or wings." It also moves the arm by adducting the humorus (bringing the arm towards the sides of the body).

c) **Deltoid muscle:** this muscle moves the humorus but it abducts the arm (bringing the arm away from the sides of the body and upwards). It accounts for the roundness of the shoulder. The word "delta" means triangle and indeed the deltoid muscle is triangular.

VI. Forearm Extensors and Flexors: these muscles cross the elbow joint.

a) **Posterior compartment**: here we find the **Triceps**. It has three heads and serves to extend the forearm. It is the only muscle of the posterior arm and is antagonistic (has the opposite function) to the biceps.

b) **Anterior compartment**: the **Biceps** flex the arm at the elbow joint and has two heads. It is one of the muscles in the anterior compartment.

VII. Muscles of the Thigh

a) **Anterior Thigh muscles**

1. **Quadriceps**: this muscle is found in the anterior thigh and has four heads. It makes up the flesh of the front and side of the thigh. These muscles are the most powerful muscles of the body. They are individually named the **Rectus femoris, and the Lateral, Medial, and Intermediate Vastus.** They extend the knee for climbing, jumping, or running. All four heads insert into the quadriceps tendon which in turn encases the patella and then the tendon goes to the tibia.

2. **Sartorius Muscle**: this is a strap like muscle which runs obliquely across the anterior surface of the thigh to the knee. It is also the longest muscle in the body. It flexes the leg and thigh and is used to sit down with your legs crossed, "Indian style". A sartor is a tailor and this muscle was named after them because they sit down "Indian style" in order to pin up the hems of skirts and pants.

b) **Posterior Thigh Muscles**

1. Here we have the **Hamstrings** which include the **Biceps Femoris, Semitendinosus and the Semimembranosus**. All three flex the knee joint. These muscles account for the fleshiness of the posterior thigh and they are innervated by the sciatic nerve. The sciatic nerve is the longest nerve in the body. It begins in the lower back, then goes through the buttocks and down the leg. The name "hamstrings" arises from the old butchers' practice of using the tendons of the ham (posterior thigh) to hang it up for smoking. Pulled hamstrings are a very common sports injury for those who run very hard.

2. **Muscles of the Buttocks** are also in the posterior thigh:

Gluteus Maximus: this muscle forms the buttocks and extends from the pelvis to the thigh. It is situated over the sciatic nerve.

Gluteus Medius: this muscle is deep and superior to the gluteus maximus. Therefore, it is a frequent site to administer an intramuscular injection because there is no chance of hitting the sciatic nerve.

Gluteus Minimus: this is the smallest and deepest gluteal muscle.

The Gluteal Muscles are also involved with rotating the thigh.

c) Medial Thigh muscles

The **Gracilis** is a medial thigh muscle that moves the thigh. Actually it adducts the thigh at the hip joint so it is used while horseback riding (brings the legs together). It is long and thin and it is the muscle in the groin.

VIII. Leg

The leg is involved with ankle and toe movement.

Posterior and Superficial Leg Muscle: The Gastrocnemius muscle accounts for the curve of the calf and it flexes the foot. Distally, this muscle forms **Achilles tendon** which inserts on the heel bone of the foot called the calcaneous bone.

Anabolic Steroids

History: Athletes

> 1960s to increase performance

Engineered by drug companies

> 1930s
>> Like testosterone
>> Drug related to testosterone

Availability

> Gyms/competitions
>
> Mail order
>
> Smuggled
>
> Felony
>
> Counterfeit products

Endogenous Testosterone causes:

> 1. Increase in muscle mass - the fibers get thicker
>
> 2. Increase bone mass
>
> 3. Responsible for secondary male sex traits

Legitimate uses:

> 1950s:
>> Anemia
>>
>> Muscle wasting
>>
>> Patients immobilized
>>
>> Reduced/absent testicular function
>>
>> Severe burns
>>
>> Breast cancer
>
>> However, they are seldom prescribed today

Used by:

> Professional body builders
>
> Shot put, discus throwers
>
> Football players

Advantages:

      Increase mass (muscle size)

      Increase in strength

      Enhanced RBC volume

      Improves endurance

      Decreases recovery time between workouts

      Increases aggressive behavior

Dosage/Usage:

      High doses and heavy resistance training

      Begin before competition, then increased as the event nears

      Administered with a high protein diet

      Modes of use

            Scheduled Cycle:

            Pyramiding:

            Stacking:

Signs of steroid use:

      Weight gain

      Muscle gain

      Aggressiveness

      Combativeness

      Jaundice

      Spots on body

      Swelling

      Trembling

      Breath odor

Adverse Effects:

Damage to reproductive organs:

  Reduced sexual function:

      1. Males

            Shriveled testes

            Infertility

      2. Females

            More body hair

Deeper voice

Smaller breasts

Fewer menstrual cycles

Irreversible masculine traits

Sterility

3. Adolescents

Stunted growth

Liver damage

Increases blood cholesterol levels

Elevated blood pressure } most seriously affected

Cardiovascular damage

Bloated face

Severe acne

Premature balding

Mental problems

Manic behavior

Violence

"Roid Rage"

Depression

Delusions

Steroids boost athletic performance and they are called "**the gear**". Anabolic steroid use became a felony for non medical use and distribution in 1989. There are a number of bogus or counterfeit products sold today. The actual steroids can be diverted from pharmacies and are also fabricated in underground laboratories.

Endogenous (produced in the body) **testosterone** causes the physical changes associated with male puberty (enlargement of the larynx, penis, testicles, the appearance of pubic hair and a beard etc…).

After World War II, it was believed that steroids were a good drug to treat burn victims since they were believed to stimulate tissue growth. This is no longer the accepted opinion. They are used however, in patients with HIV infection who have muscle wasting.

In addition to body builders and other athletes, they are also illegitimately used by people who have **muscular dysmorphia syndrome**. These individuals have a distorted image of their body. No matter how muscular they are (and they have large muscles), they think they look small and weak.

In any event, when a user stops taking steroids they tend to lose most of what they gained. However, they do reduce body fat and increase muscle definition.

There are different ways to use steroids:

1. **Scheduled** cycle: 6 - 12 weeks on steroids, followed by a period of abstinence which allows the body time to adjust; it gives the hormonal system time to recuperate.

2. **Pyramiding** is when one slowly escalates the doseage reaching a peak at mid-cycle. Then the dosage is gradually tapered off towards the end of the cycle.

3. **Stacking** drugs is using multiple drugs concurrently (for example, using both oral and intramuscular steroids). This cocktail produces effects on muscle size greater than the effect of using each drug separately.

To help return the levels of "test" (testosterone) back to normal, some individuals take **HCG** (human chorionic gonadotropin) which in the male promotes the secretion of endogenous testosterone.

Some take steroids with **HGH** (human growth hormone) because this hormone helps build up muscles and shred away fat at the same time. It causes growth.

Insulin is also taken since these individuals want to consume over 6,000 calories per day. After the injection they eat a lot of carbohydrates (sugars) because insulin assists glucose entry into the cells.

The adverse affects seen in steroid users include damage to the reproductive organs. In the male, **testicular atrophy** often ensues accompanied with **infertility**. Men also develop more breast tissue and their nipples enlarge (**gynecomastia**). Premature balding occurs (**male pattern baldness**). In female users there is a **masculinizing effect**: the clitoris enlarges and swells making it appear as a small penis.

The most seriously affected organs are the **liver** (cancer, increased cholesterol levels), and **heart** (coronary heart disease).

There has been a significant increase in the use of steroids among high school students, university students and young adults.

Some of the common oral steroids are **Anadrol**, **Dianobol**, and **Winstrol**. The most widely used injectable steroids are **Deca-Durabolin**, **Depo-Testosterone**, and **Equipose**.

_____

Last Name, First Name

General Biology
Dr. Abdirkin

Review Questions

36. Where is the human egg fertilized?

37. In the male, where are the dartos and cremaster muscles? What do they do?

38. Explain how a doctor checks for an inguinal hernia in a male.

39. Explain why the increased blood supply to the penis during erection does not cause the penis to keep swelling and swelling until it bursts.

40. Does a vasectomy affect male potency?

41. Are most muscles paired?

42. An eyebrow is drawn toward the midline of the face through the contraction of which muscle?

43. What is the function of the rectus abdominis muscle?

Digestive System / Alimentary Canal / Gastrointestinal (GI) Tract 19

The GI tract is a long continuous muscular tube, which is situated in the ventral cavity of the body. It is open at both ends (mouth and anus). The salivary glands, liver, gallbladder and pancreas all produce and store digestive secretions. As food travels through the canal it gets chopped, mashed, mixed, churned and bathed in chemicals (enzymes). Everything of value is extracted and the residue is ejected (feces).

Function

Food is broken down in smaller fragments so the GI tract acts like a *disassembly* line. Next these particles are absorbed into the blood and carried to the cells so that they may be used for metabolic processes. Therefore, nutrients become available to the body.

Activities

1. **Ingestion**: this is when food enters the mouth

2. **Propulsion**: this is the movement of food and it involves:
   a) **swallowing** or deglutition. This is the passage of food from the mouth to the throat.

   b) **peristalsis** is the contraction of the smooth muscles along the entire tract. These contractions in turn push the food forward through the canal.

3. **Mechanical Processing**:
   a) **physical manipulation** occurs in the mouth. The mechanical breakdown of food begins here and this is accomplished by both the tongue and teeth.

   b) **churning** is the mixing and agitation of the contents in the stomach.

   c) **segmentation** movements are local constrictions. These churn, mix and swirl the food with enzymes in the small intestines.

   Note: both churning and segmentation movements do not propel the food forward.

4. **Chemical Digestion**:
   Chemical digestion occurs from the mouth to the small intestine. It involves **enzymatic** hydrolysis, which, converts macromolecules to micro-molecules (proteins are broken down to amino acids, fats to fatty acids and starches to sugars) so that they may be absorbed. The enzymes are secreted into the lumen of the tract by glands (salivary, liver, and pancreas).

5. **Absorption**:
   Absorption involves the movement of the end products of digestion (micro-molecules) from the lumen of the small intestine across the epithelial lining to the blood stream as well as the lymphatic system.

6. **Excretion**:

The elimination of undigested substances is called **excretion**. These substances get compacted in the large intestine and then the feces are discharged through the anus by a process called **defecation**.

Lumen of tract:

1. The inner lining of the tract is **folded**. The purpose of these folds is to increase the surface area for absorption and also to enable portions of the tract to expand after meals.

2. On these folds are **villi**. These are finger-like projections, which further increase the surface area for absorption. The villi cover the entire folded surface. They are 0.5 to 1.5 mm in length and give the intestinal lining a velvety appearance. Inside each villus are capillaries and lymph vessels (lacteals). The surface of each villus is lined with epithelial cells. The plasma membrane of each epithelial cell has microscopic projections called **microvilli**.

The folding and projections (both villi and microvilli) give the intestinal wall a surface area 600 times that of a smooth tube of the same length or a surface area of 2,200 square feet (about the size of a tennis court).

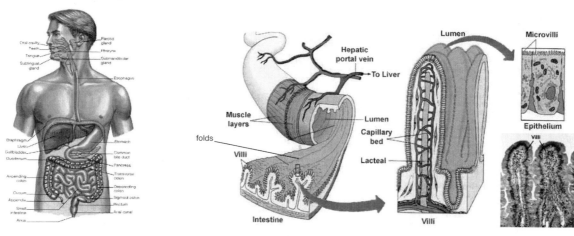

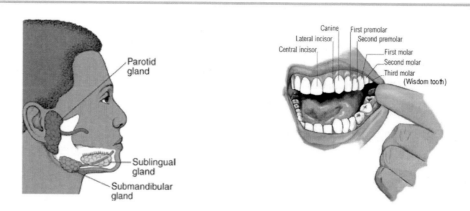

I. Oral Cavity

In the mouth food is analyzed, processed and lubricated for **swallowing**.

Components of the oral cavity:

Tongue: is for chewing, swallowing and sensory analysis. The taste buds have sensory receptors to identify the type and quality of food. The tongue manipulates the food into a mass (bolus) and presses it backwards into the pharynx.

Teeth are also involved in chewing and the mechanical breakdown of the connective tissue and fibers, which are found in many foods. The **premolars** and **molars** have flat surfaces for grinding the food into a paste. The **incisors**, which are flat, are for biting. The pointed **canines** tear food. Humans have 32 teeth of varying shapes and sizes (heterodonts).

Salivary glands:

1. produce **secretions, which consist of saliva**, and **mucus**, which begins the chemical digestion of food. Saliva contains anti-bodies, enzymes and buffers. The secretions serve to (a) **lubricate** the food and mouth; (b) **coat** the food; (c) **flush out** the oral cavity of bacteria since it contains anti-bodies as well as **lysozymes** to help guard against infection; and (d) allow **swallowing** to occur.

2. produce an **enzyme** called **amylase**. Amylase breaks down starches into simple sugars. The enzyme amylase works best at a pH of 7.5, which is slightly basic.

3. produce **buffers** to neutralize any acids.

There are **three salivary glands**. The sight, smell, taste and thought of food transmits nervous signals, which cause the secretion of saliva. These signals also cause the secretion of HCl and gastrin, which are produced in the stomach. Therefore, the stomach is notified that food is arriving.

II. Pharynx

The pharynx is a passageway for solid and liquid food as well as air. Therefore, it is both a **digestive** and **respiratory** chamber. It extends from the **internal nostrils** to the esophagus therefore, it connects the mouth to the esophagus. There are muscles, which surround the pharynx called the **pharyngeal muscles** and they assist, in the swallowing process (**deglutition**). Food is prevented from entering the windpipe (**trachea**) because the **glottis** (the opening into the larynx) is closed off during swallowing. Actually, the **larynx** moves upwards and the **epiglottis**, which is a tongue-like flap, made of cartilage moves downwards covering the entrance to the glottis. Food is thus directed into the esophagus rather than the larynx.

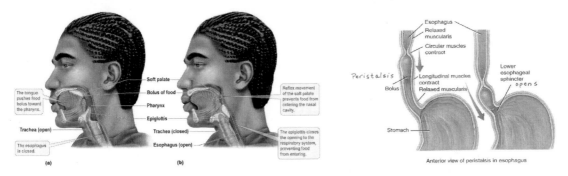

III. Esophagus

The esophagus is a muscular tube that extends from the **pharynx** to the **stomach**. It is about 1 foot long. There are two **sphincters** in the esophagus: the **upper** and **lower** sphincter. The lower one is called the **cardiac sphincter**. A sphincter is a circular muscular band, which separates different parts of the digestive system. The sphincter may be open or closed. When it is closed it prevents food from going backwards or from being **regurgitated**. The esophageal muscles contract above the bolus in sequence, squeezing it down towards the stomach. This is called **peristalsis**. The cells, which line the esophagus, secrete mucus to protect it from abrasion and also lubricate the food.

IV. Stomach

The stomach is situated in the upper left part of the abdomen. It is "J-shaped". When completely filled it may hold about 1.5 quarts to a gallon of material. It has a muscular wall and folds that allow the stomach to expand.

The **functions of the stomach** are to:

1. **store food**

2. **agitate** (mechanical) **the food** which is called **churning**-breaks apart large pieces of food

3. **secrete gastric juices** (gastric glands)-to break down proteins

4. **form chyme** (viscous soup). This consists of partially digested food and secretions.

The stomach releases food gradually into the small intestines at a suitable rate for digestion and absorption to occur in the next segment (duodenum). As food arrives in the stomach, its walls are stretched causing (a) mucus production, (b) the release of gastrin (which in turn stimulates) the secretion of (c) HCl and the (d) secretion of pepsinogen:

The **gastric glands** are located in the gastric wall and they secrete:

a) **hydrochloric acid** (HCl), which is as strong as battery acid. It has a pH of about 2 (very acidic).

b) **pepsinogen** (which is an inactive substance). Pepsinogen is converted to **pepsin** under the influence of HCl. Pepsin is a **proteolytic enzyme**, which means that it digests proteins.

c) **gastrin** when the stomach **distends** due to the arrival of food and also because the **pH** of stomach increases. Gastrin is a hormone and is released from the stomach into the blood. It circulates around in the blood stream like any other hormone. Eventually, it will make its way back to the stomach and stimulates the gastric glands to secrete more HCl and more pepsinogen. Therefore, gastrin regulates the activities of the stomach.

d) **mucus** coats the stomach lining and serves as a barrier against self-digestion from the HCl and pepsin.

Peristaltic waves propel the chyme from the stomach towards the small intestine. There is a sphincter at the end of the stomach called the **pyloric sphincter**. It regulates the release of the chyme from the stomach to the small intestine. Therefore, the pyloric sphincter is involved with **gastric emptying**. In addition, **intestinal hormones** and a **nervous reflex** regulate gastric emptying. Only a teaspoon of chyme is expelled with each contraction. It takes about 3 hours to empty the stomach.

No **absorption** occurs in stomach, however **alcohol** may enter the blood stream through the stomach wall. If the stomach is empty, alcohol gets absorbed immediately into the blood and has a strong and rapid effort. This is why it is not a good idea "to drink on an empty stomach".

Since the stomach is involved with churning and mixing the food contents (power movements), it is made up of **three muscle layers**, one on top of the other. This is the only place in the digestive system where there are three muscular layers. The other parts of the tract only have two layers.

A **hiatal hernia** is when the superior part of the stomach pushes upwards through an enlarged **esophageal hiatus**. The esophageal hiatus is an opening in the **diaphragm**. The diaphragm is the large dome-shaped muscle that separates the thorax from the abdomen. This opening provides a passageway normally for the esophagus as it descends from the thorax into the abdominal cavity. If there is a weakening of the diaphragmatic muscle fibers around the hiatus, the hiatus enlarges permitting the upper part of the stomach to move up into the thorax. Because the diaphragm no longer reinforces the action of the cardiac sphincter, the acidic stomach juices are persistently **regurgitated**, eroding the wall of the esophagus, which causes a burning pain. This is called **gastro-esophageal reflux disease (GERD)**.

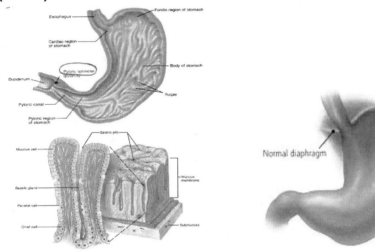
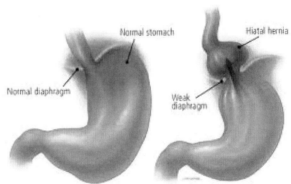

V. Small Intestine

The small intestine is about 22 feet long and packed into the peritoneal cavity. It is about 1.5 inches in diameter. The **functions of the small intestine** include the:

1. **neutralization** of acids (pancreatic buffers)
2. **emulsification** of fats (bile)
3. **digestion** of proteins (pancreatic enzymes)
4. **digestion** of carbohydrates (pancreatic enzymes)

Digestion and absorption occur in the small intestine with the secretions from the liver, gallbladder, pancreas and intestinal cells. In fact, most digestion occurs in the small intestine. It is **subdivided** into the:

1. **Duodenum**, which is the proximal portion, about one foot long and receives the chyme from the stomach. Enzymatic reactions occur here and this is where the absorption of sugars, amino acids and fats occur.
2. **Jejunum** is eight feet long and is also involved with the absorption of sugars, amino acids and fats. This segment follows the duodenum.
3. **Ileum** is the last thirteen feet. The **ileocecal valve** is located at the distal end of the ileum to control the flow of chyme into the **cecum** (large intestine). It is in the ileum where

vitamins and electrolytes are absorbed.

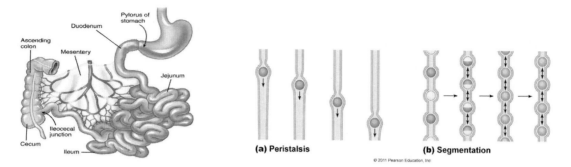

(a) Peristalsis   (b) Segmentation

© 2011 Pearson Education, Inc.

Intestinal Movements:

1. **Local segmentation** or random contractions of the intestinal muscles enable the contents to be mixed with the digestive enzymes. These local segmentations do not move the contents forward, rather they only mix and swirl the food with enzymes.

2. **Peristalsis** on the other hand does move the contents forward.

It usually takes **five hours** for material to go from the duodenum to the end of the ileum.

Intestinal Secretions:

About 2 liters of intestinal fluid is secreted per day. This fluid contains:

1. **Mucus,** which is secreted by the intestinal glands, located at the base of the villi

2. **Hormones** are released from the duodenum which in turn stimulate the release of the digestive enzymes from the pancreas and gallbladder. These hormones include:

    a) **Secretin,** which is released into blood when the acidic chyme arrives. Secretin then stimulates the release of buffers (bicarbonate) from the pancreas, which are sent to the small intestine to neutralize the acids.

    b) **CCK** is released from the intestines into the blood also and then it stimulates the:

        1. **gallbladder** to contract, ejecting **bile salts** into the intestine, which **emulsify** fats

        2. **pancreas** to release the **pancreatic enzymes,** which will digest complex carbohydrates and proteins

3. **GIP** (gastric inhibitory peptide) is also released which inhibits gastric secretions and gastric activity in general (i.e. decreases motion) so that the small intestine has time to catch up, before any more material is emptied into it from the stomach.

Intestinal Wall: recall the structures of the intestinal lumen (page 144) for absorption:

1. **villi** are finger-like projections, which contain:

    a) **capillaries** to absorb the nutrients and transport them to the liver (**portal circulation**)

    b) **lacteals** (lymph vessels), which are involved with fat processing and absorption

2. **microvilli** carpet the villi and further increase the surface area of the small intestine. They are minute projections of the plasma membranes of the cells that line the villi. Recall, both

the villi and microvilli increase the surface area of the intestine for absorption.

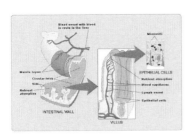 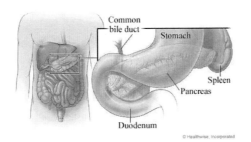 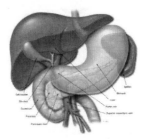

Digestion is completed in the small intestine, yielding **sugars**, **fatty acids** and **amino acids**, which are then absorbed into the blood stream. Energy is expended to transport these nutrients into the intestinal cells. Then by diffusion these monomers get into the capillaries or lacteals. Most of these substances go to the liver next. The **enzymes** and **buffers**, which work in the small intestine, come from the **pancreas** and **liver** (gallbladder).

VI. Pancreas

The pancreas is located behind the stomach. It is an elongated organ and the length is about 6 inches. The pancreas is considered both an exocrine and endocrine gland.

1. **Exocrine organ**
   Certain pancreatic cells produce and secrete the pancreatic juices, which are sent to the duodenum via ducts. These secretions consist of:

   a) **Buffers** like **sodium bicarbonate** ($NaCO_3$) to neutralize the acidic chyme.

   b) **Enzymes**, which are secreted in an "inactive form" called **proenzymes** or **zymogens**. The reason they are secreted this way is to prevent auto-digestion. In other words, if these enzymes were secreted in their activated formula they would digest the pancreas itself. However, these proenzymes are activated only when they reach the intestines by the **enterokinases**. Some of the pancreatic enzymes are:

      1. **amylase**, which is involved in carbohydrate digestion

      2. **lipase** is for fat digestion

      3. **nucleases** digest DNA and RNA

      4. **proteases** digest proteins

2. **Endocrine gland**
   As an endocrine gland, there are specialized cells (about 1% of the total number of cells) in the pancreas, which make **insulin**. Insulin is a hormone that is secreted into the blood to control the **glucose concentration** in the blood stream (blood sugar).

VII. Liver

The liver is the largest **visceral organ** weighing about three pounds. It has many functions. The liver has a **limited regenerative capacity** and is divided into four lobes. The liver cells are called **hepatocytes**. The liver produces **bile**, which is stored in the **gallbladder**. Bile is released into the small intestine (duodenum) through a tube called the **bile duct**. Bile is made up of bile salts, water, and cholesterol. The bile salts act like **detergents**, which break fats apart into smaller particles (**emulsification**) so they can be digested by **lipase** (pancreas) and then absorbed. The smaller fat subunits then enter into the intestinal cells where they are coated with proteins before entering the **lacteals** (lymph vessels).

Complex macromolecules during the digestive process enter the small intestine where they are broken down into micronutrients, which in turn are absorbed into the blood system. All of the blood from the digestive system, which contains these basic monomers like glucose, amino acids, fatty acids and vitamins, goes to the liver (via the **hepatic portal system**). The liver utilizes some of these substances. The rest go with the blood through the blood vessels to the heart. The lungs then oxygenate this blood. The oxygen plus these monomers go into the systemic circulation and are taken to all of the cells in the body. The cells use these nutrients to carry out their metabolic activities.

Major functions of the Liver:

1. **metabolic regulation**: absorbs nutrients and toxins. It also adjusts the level of nutrients in the blood (i.e. glucose and glycogen).

2. **blood regulation**: the liver is the largest **blood reservoir**. It removes old and damaged RBCs, makes plasma proteins as well as the components of the clotting mechanism.

3. **bile production**: synthesizes and secretes bile for fat digestion. The bile is stored in the **gallbladder**. The gallbladder is situated in a recess under the right liver lobe. It is a sac which stores and concentrates bile.

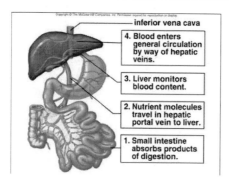
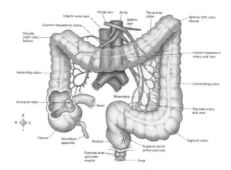

VIII. Large Intestine (Bowel)

The large intestine is horseshoe-shaped, located below the stomach and liver, and it frames the small intestine. It is about five feet long with a circumference of three inches. The large intestine extends from the end of the ileum (small intestine) to the anus. There are three regions:

1. **Cecum** - pouch or rounded sac. This is an expanded chamber at the beginning of the large intestine. The **ileocecal valve** is located at the junction between the ileum and cecum. It is here that we also find the **vermiform appendix**, which is about 3.5 inches long and is attached at the postero-medial surface of the cecum. The appendix is actually **lymphoid** tissue.

2. **Colon**- largest portion. It contains the **haustrae**, which are external pouches. These permit distension and elongation of the large intestine when it is full. The **taenia coli** are external longitudinal bands of muscle. The colon consists of four portions:

   a) **ascending** colon, which extends from the ileocecal value and goes upwards along the right side of the abdominal cavity to reach the inferior margin of the liver.

   b) **transverse** colon is the next portion and is located below the stomach. It begins as the ascending colon starts to make a left turn and then goes across to the left side of the abdominal cavity near the spleen.

  c) **descending** colon begins as the colon makes an inferior turn and descends along the left side of the cavity.

  d) **sigmold** colon is a shaped like an "s". It connects the descending colon to the rectum.

 3. **Rectum** - is about six inches long. It **prepares and stores** fecal material until **defecation** (elimination). It is the last segment of the tract and consists of **columnar epithelium**. The very last part of the rectum is the **anal canal** or also called the **anorectal canal**. This canal contains both longitudinal and transverse folds on the inside. It is made up of **stratified squamous epithelium** just like the oral cavity. The **anus** is the opening of this canal to the outside and consists of a **keratinized epidermis** like the skin. There are two sphincters, which control defecation. The **internal sphincter** is under **autonomic** control (involuntary) and is made up of smooth muscle. The **external sphincter** guards the exit of the anus. This sphincter is made of skeletal muscle and so it is under **voluntary** control. Therefore, the individual is able to control the external muscular sphincter and relaxes it when it is convenient to defecate.

The leftovers of digestion (water, undigested fats and fibers) enter the large intestine.

Functions of the Colon:

1. **Reabsorption** of water to compact and prepare the feces. Think of it as a compacter. 1.5 liters of water arrive in the colon every day. 1.3 liters of this water is reabsorbed. The difference, which is about 150 - 200 ml, is ejected with the feces. This represents 75% of the feces however, the feces also contains undigested material, inorganic material and damaged cells which account for 20% or 40 ml. The remaining 5% or 10 ml of the feces consists of bacteria.

2. **Absorption** of vitamins and other substances

  a) there are **bacteria** in the colon, which produce **vitamins B_{12} and K**. These vitamins are absorbed. There are other bacteria that live in the colon which produce **odors** and **gas**.

  b) **bile salts** are reabsorbed at this level and then returned to liver

3. **Defecation**- when the stomach distends after a meal it causes **powerful peristaltic contractions** in the colon called "**mass movement**". This movement sweeps over the entire colon forcing the feces into the rectum and eventually causing an urge to defecate. Even though the external sphincter closes automatically with the **defecation reflex** remember it can be relaxed voluntarily when it is appropriate to defecate. To defecate, an individual applies pressure which forces blood into the veins of the submucosa of the anorectal canal. Repeated, stressful forcing may cause these vessels to stretch and eventually become permanently distended. This is a condition called **hemorrhoids**.

Diarrhea is frequent watery bowel movements due to either the:

1. colonic mucosa not able to maintain normal **absorption** or the

2. rate of **fluid entry** into colon is greater than its reabsorption capacity.

Some of the causes of diarrhea are **bacteria, viruses, and protozoa**. For example, the **cholera bacteria** bind to the lining of the intestine and release toxins, which cause massive fluid secretion into the intestine. This causes a severe fluid and ion loss leading to acute dehydration, which may result in death.

Constipation is just the opposite of diarrhea-infrequent defecation. In this case, there is very slow fecal movement, which leads to **excessive water reabsorption**. Therefore, the feces become dry, hard and abrasive. The slow fecal movement is usually due to inadequate **dietary** fiber, inadequate **fluid** intake or a lack of **exercise**.

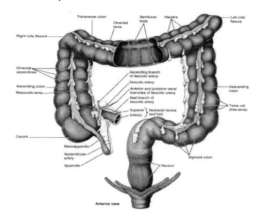

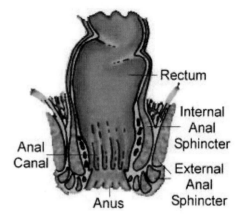

Respiratory System

20

Introduction

Our cells obtain energy through the process of respiration and this requires oxygen. Inside of the lungs diffusion occurs between the external air and the blood. The blood becomes re-oxygenated as it passes through the lungs and simultaneously carbon dioxide is expelled. The respiratory system is assisted by the circulatory system, which transports oxygen to the tissues. At the tissue level, carbon dioxide and wastes are removed, enter into circulation and are taken back to the lungs to be expelled to the atmosphere.

**Respiration** is involved with:
1. gas exchange
2. smell perception
3. air filtration
4. sound production
5. waste elimination

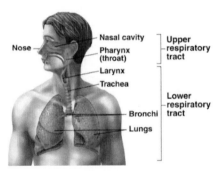

I. Overview

Respiration is defined as the exchange of gases between the cells and the atmosphere via the blood. It involves three steps:

1. **pulmonary ventilation**, which is simply normal breathing. This includes **inspiration** or the inflow of air and **expiration** or the outflow of air.

2. **pulmonary respiration** is the exchange of gases between the lungs and the blood.

3. **internal or tissue respiration** is the exchange of gases between the blood and tissue cells. The blood gives up the oxygen it is carrying to the tissues and the tissues release carbon dioxide to the blood.

There are two portions to the respiratory system:

1. The **upper part,** which includes the nose and pharynx (throat).

2. The **lower portion**, which includes the larynx (voice box), trachea (windpipe), bronchi, and lungs.

Otorhinolaryngology = the study of the ears, nose and throat, also called **ENT**.

II. Organs

A) **Nose**: the external nose is a framework of **bone, cartilage, skin and muscle**. The structure of these components make the nose very flexible. The **external nares** (nostrils) is the name given to the two openings on the under surface of the nose. The internal nose communicates with the pharynx and is divided into equal halves by the **nasal septum**.

The **functions** of the nose are to:

1. warm, moisten and filter the incoming **air** of dust and pathogens

2. receives **olfactory** stimuli

3. modify **speech**

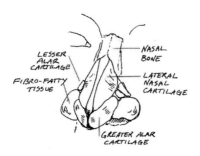
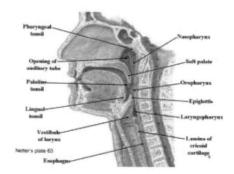

The internal nose is lined with **respiratory epithelium**. The columnar epithelial cells, which make up this type of epithelium, are ciliated. The cilia move dust and mucus towards the pharynx so they may be eliminated by either **expectoration** or swallowing. There is also **olfactory epithelium** present that relays sensory information to the nervous system so that smell perception is realized.

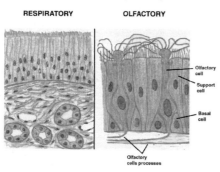
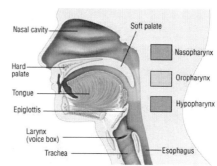

B) **Pharynx**: The pharynx is about 5 inches long. It extends from the **internal nares** to the **larynx** and is subdivided into three parts:

1. **Naso-pharynx,** which is situated just behind the nose

2. **Oro-pharynx,** which is behind the mouth

3. **Laryngo-pharynx,** which is in the proximity of the larynx

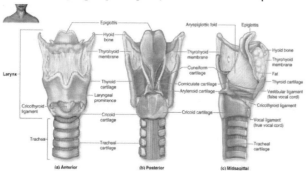
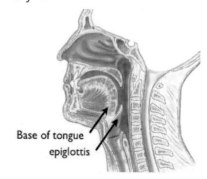

C) Larynx: The larynx connects the laryngopharynx (the last part of the pharynx) to the **trachea**. There is a very obvious bulge on the external neck just below the chin, which is made up of **thyroid cartilage** and is commonly called the **Adam's apple** or the voice box. This is the larynx. Usually the Adam's apple is larger in males however, it is shield-shaped in both sexes. But why is it called an Adam's apple? Well, just think of the story about the Garden of Eden where Adam ate a piece of the forbidden fruit that got stuck in his throat. Since this bulge sometimes looks like a small, rounded apple just under the skin in the front of the throat, it was given the name Adam's apple. When swallowing, the whole larynx moves up and the **epiglottis** seals off the entrance, which leads into the larynx (this opening is called the **glottis**). The epiglottis is a leaf-shaped piece of **elastic cartilage**. It looks similar to the tongue but it may move up and down like a trap door. Therefore, the epiglottis prevents food from entering the lungs. Refer to the previous figure to visualize these structures for a better understanding. The **vocal cords** are located inside the larynx. They extend from the **arytenoid cartilages**, and then go across the diameter of the **larynx** to the thyroid cartilage. There are two sets of cords actually and they are called the **true and false cords**. The **true vocal cords** are ligaments that cause sound production. The **false cords** are situated above the true ones and serve to protect the true cords. They prevent foreign objects from damaging the true cords.

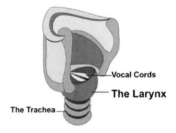

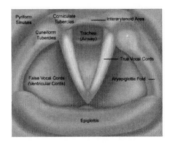

Voice
Sound production is due to the vibrations of the cords as air passes past them. These vibrations generate sound waves. The volume of sound and its resonance are due to the sinuses, pharynx, oral and nasal cavities. Word production is due to the movement of the tongue, cheeks, and lips. The ability to speak is under voluntary control.

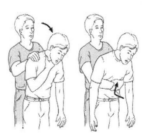

Heimlich Maneuver
Sometimes a foreign object may become lodged in the larynx. If the victim cannot expel the obstruction by coughing then the situation may become life threatening. If another individual applies compression just below the diaphragm, this action will elevate the diaphragm and hopefully generate enough pressure to remove the blockage by forcing it upwards and out of the throat. If the blockage still remains, then an incision (by a qualified professional) is made through the anterior tracheal wall below the blockage. A tube is then inserted to permit airflow. This procedure is called a **tracheostomy**.

D) Trachea (wind pipe): The trachea is a flexible tube which has a diameter of approximately 1 inch and a length of 4 inches. Its walls are made up of **"C"- shaped cartilage rings** to protect the tube. The trachea bifurcates (branches) at the level of the 5th thoracic vertebrae to make up the two **primary bronchi.**

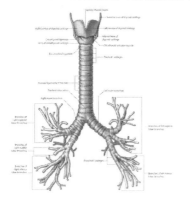

Right main bronchus is wider, shorter, runs more vertically.
X= Anular ligament/Tracheal ligament between adjacent tracheal cartilages.

Alveoli

E) Bronchial Tree

primary bronchi - there is a left and right bronchus
secondary bronchi - further branching
tertiary bronchi - more branching but the rings get smaller
bronchioles - the next division and these are very narrow
terminal bronchioles - additional branching
respiratory bronchioles - the finest branches and open up into the alveoli
alveoli - expansive chambers at the end of all this branching. The alveoli contain the
respiratory membranes - the area between the blood capillaries and the alveoli of the lung tissue. This membrane is the location of gas exchange.

F) Lobules: the lungs are divided into lobules, which are the basic structures of this organ. Each lobule is made up of one terminal bronchiole, several respiratory bronchioles, several alveoli, one arteriole, one venule, and a capillary network.

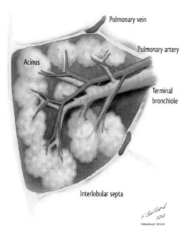

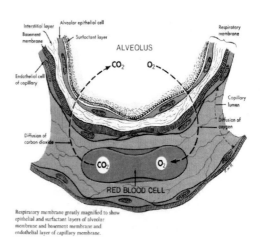

Respiratory membrane greatly magnified to show epithelial and surfactant layers of alveolar membrane and basement membrane and endothelial layer of capillary membrane.

G) Respiratory Membrane: this membrane is the area where gas exchange actually takes place. It is made up of capillaries of the circulatory system, which are adjacent to the alveoli. In fact, the cells of each area are cemented together. In addition, **macrophages** are inside the alveoli. The macrophages are called **dust cells** and their function is to patrol the alveoli. Whenever they encounter any dust or debris they engulf these particles and break them down to avoid any damage to the lungs. This exchange surface is about the size of a tennis court when considering all of the alveoli in both lungs.

H) Lungs: There are two lungs in the human, a **left** and **right lung**. The lungs are further subdivided into lobes. The lobes are large sections of each lung. The right lung is made of three lobes but the left has only two lobes because the heart occupies space (**cardiac notch**). The lungs are very light, have a spongy appearance and their volume consists of air.

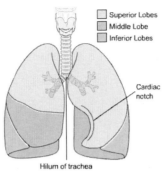

III. Respiratory Function

There are **four steps** involved in respiration. The **first** is breathing which is a physical action (**pulmonary ventilation**). In the **second** step, there is **gas diffusion** across the respiratory membrane in the alveoli. This brings in oxygen and releases the carbon dioxide to the atmosphere (**gas exchange**). The **third** step involves the transport and storage of oxygen and carbon dioxide in the blood (through the blood vessels) by the circulatory system (**storage and transport**). In the last or **fourth step**, there is another exchange of oxygen and carbon dioxide between the blood and the tissues (**gas exchange**). Recall that oxygen is taken to the tissues and carbon dioxide is removed. Next we will discuss each one of these steps in more detail.

1. **Pulmonary Ventilation:** this is breathing which involves the physical movement of air in and out of the lungs. In one breath, which is called the **respiratory cycle** there is one inspiration and one expiration.

   Breathing Modes

   a) **quiet breathing** involves the muscular contractions of the diaphragm for **inhalation. Exhalation** is a passive process, which occurs due to the recoil of the diaphragm.

   b) **forced breathing** occurs when both inhalation and exhalation are active. In other words, additional muscles of the rib cage are employed besides the diaphragm. For example, when the uterus is enlarged (pregnancy), it causes the other organs in the abdomen to push up against the diaphragm-breathing requires an extra effort so more muscles are required.

   The **tidal volume** is the amount of air moved in or out of the lungs during one respiratory cycle. This is approximately ½ quart (500 ml).

2. **Gas Exchange** at the level of:

   a) **pulmonary capillaries** (respiratory membrane) which are in the lungs

   b) **systemic capillaries** which are in the body tissues at the cellular level

   Oxygen in the air enters the nasal cavity. Then it passes through the pharynx, larynx, bronchial tree, and finally gets into the alveoli. The oxygen diffuses from these spaces across the respiratory membrane and enters into the blood stream. It is then carried by the blood cells to the tissues of the body via the circulatory system. When the blood arrives at the tissues, the oxygen diffuses from the red blood cells to the cells of the body. On the other hand, carbon dioxide leaves the tissues and enters into the blood. The circulatory system brings the carbon dioxide to the lungs. Then carbon dioxide leaves the blood, crosses the respiratory membrane and arrives in the alveoli. Next it is expelled outside of the body to the air by the process of exhalation.

3. Gas Storage and Transport

Blood carries the gases (carbon dioxide and oxygen) to the body tissues as well as storing them.

a) **Oxygen transport:** most of the oxygen molecules bind to **hemoglobin** which is a large globular protein inside of red blood cells. Hemoglobin has four pockets in which oxygen molecules may attach themselves. In other words, four oxygen molecules are carried by one hemoglobin protein. Inside of each hemoglobin pocket there is one iron (Fe) molecule. This is the exact location where the oxygen is carried. The arrow in the equation below has two heads, which signifies that this is a reversible reaction. The oxygen binds to Hb at the respiratory membrane; it is then transported this way (Hb-O_2) to the tissues. As the blood circulates through the tissues, the Hb releases the oxygen molecules so that they may enter into the cells (reverse reaction).

$$Hb + O_2 \longleftrightarrow Hb\text{-}O_2$$

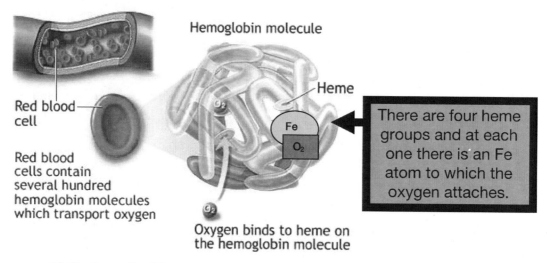

Hemoglobin molecule

Heme

Red blood cell

Red blood cells contain several hundred hemoglobin molecules which transport oxygen

Fe

O_2

There are four heme groups and at each one there is an Fe atom to which the oxygen attaches.

O_2

Oxygen binds to heme on the hemoglobin molecule

b) **Carbon dioxide transport:** carbon dioxide is generated during cellular metabolism as a waste product. It then gets into the blood and is carried to the lungs so that it may be eliminated. The transport of carbon dioxide is more complex than oxygen. There are three different ways that carbon dioxide may be transported:

1. 7% of the carbon dioxide dissolves in the plasma

2. 23% binds to hemoglobin forming **carbamino-hemoglobin:**

$$Hb + CO_2 \longleftrightarrow Hb\text{-}CO_2$$

3. 70% of the carbon dioxide combines with water in the plasma and forms a negative ion called **carbonate** which enters the red blood cell. Once inside of the RBC, the carbonate becomes **sodium bicarbonate**. Sodium bicarbonate is transported in the circulation and when it arrives in the lungs, the reverse reaction occurs so that the carbon dioxide may be released to the air.

$$CO_2 \; + \; H_2O \; \longleftrightarrow \; HCO_3^- \; \longleftrightarrow \; NaHCO_3$$

$$\text{carbonate ion} \qquad \text{sodium bicarbonate}$$
$$\text{(plasma)} \qquad\qquad \text{(RBC)}$$

IV. Respiratory Control

The brain stem is an area at the base of the brain and it connects the spinal cord to the brain. In this region, there is an area which controls breathing called the **respiratory center**. Basically, this center:

   a) regulates the **respiratory muscles** like the diaphragm

   b) controls the **number of breathes per minute**, which is called the **respiratory rate**. In the normal adult, the respiratory rate is between 12 - 15 breaths per minute. If an individual takes amphetamines, since they stimulate the central nervous system (CNS) the respiratory rate increases. Barbiturates depress the CNS thus the respiratory rate decreases.

   c) controls the **depth of breathing**

This center consists of **two parts**:

   1. **Rhythmicity center:** this portion sets the pace of respiration. It is located in the medulla.

   2. **Pons center:** this portion adjusts the rhythmicity center. It is a higher level of control

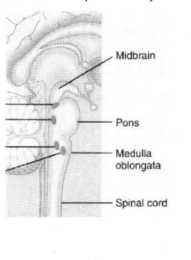

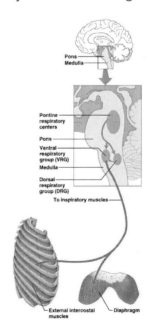

Last Name, First Name

Review Questions

44. Trace the route taken by air in the vertebrate respiratory system, listing the structures through which it flows starting with the nose or mouth to the point at which gas exchange occurs.

45. What events occur during human inhalation? Exhalation? Which of these is always an active process?

46. Describe the effects of smoking on the human respiratory system.

47. List and describe the function of the three principle secretions of the stomach.

48. Explain the defecation reflex.

49. If you added pepsinogen to a test tube containing protein dissolved in distilled water, not much protein would be digested. What inorganic substance could you add to accelerate protein digestion?

50. Explain how the epiglottis works in preventing food or drink from going down the wrong pipe?